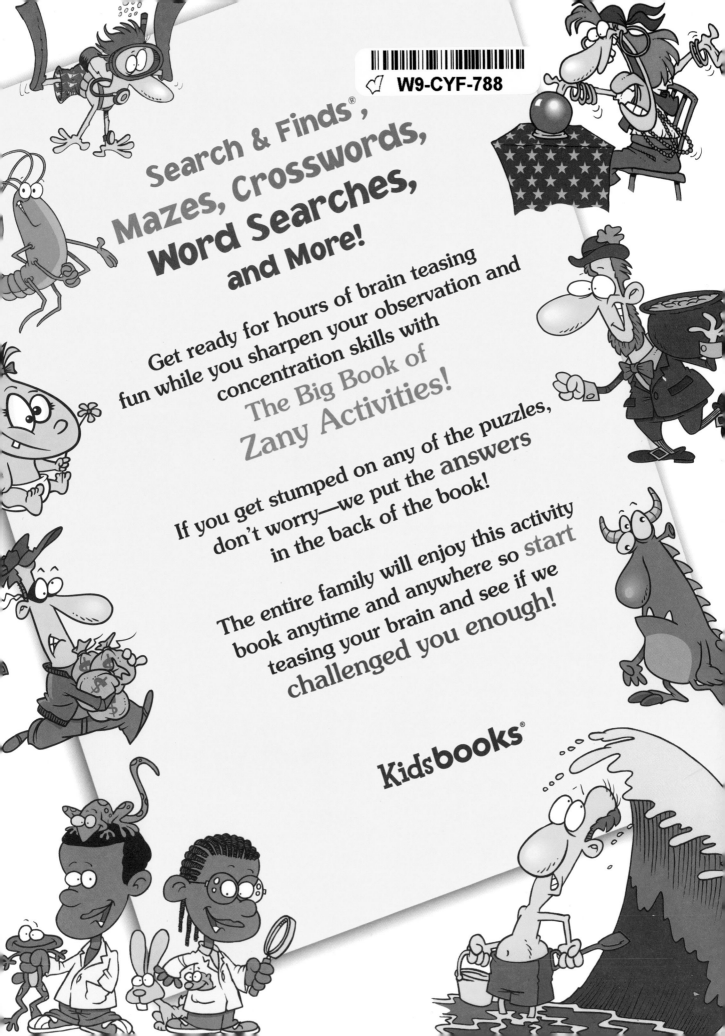

Search & Finds®,
Mazes, Crosswords,
Word Searches,
and More!

Get ready for hours of brain teasing fun while you sharpen your observation and concentration skills with
The Big Book of
Zany Activities!

If you get stumped on any of the puzzles, don't worry—we put the answers in the back of the book!

The entire family will enjoy this activity book anytime and anywhere so start teasing your brain and see if we challenged you enough!

Kidsbooks®

Rhyme Time

Find a word that rhymes with each word listed below,
using the clues in the parentheses. Then read down the column
in blue to answer the question:

"What rhymes with 'orange'?"

1) SEA (body part) _Knee_

2) HOWL (garden tool) _Trowel_

3) FIRST (explode) _Burst_

4) HARP (pointy) _Sharp_

5) HEIGHT (chew) _Bite_

6) FROWN (funny guy) _Clown_

7) SPONGE (fall) _plunge_

1. K n e e
2. t r o w e l
3. B u r s t
4. S h a r p
5. B i t e
6. c l o w n
7. p l u n g e

Answer on page 232

In Action

Use the clues below to complete this crossword puzzle about actions.

ACROSS

1 On skates, bikes, or scooters
4 Go high in the air
5 Up a tree or mountain
7 To stroll

DOWN

2 Big jump
3 Don't leave the water ____
5 Babies, before walking
6 Birds and planes and kites

1 r o l l 2 l
         l e
      3 r e
4 j u m p
      n
      n
      i
      n
5 c l i m b i n g
  r
  a 6 f
7 w a l k
  i   y
  n
  g

5

Decode-a-Riddle

Write the letter that comes **THREE LETTERS BEFORE** each letter shown below to decode and solve this riddle.

WHAT MADE
Z K D W P D G H

THE OCTOPUS
W K H   R F W R S X V

GIGGLE?
J L J J O H

EIGHT TICKLES
H L J K W W L F N O H V

Double Popsicles

Can you find the <u>two</u> pictures that are exactly alike?

Answer on page 232

Fascination

Can you make **25** words or more from this word?

FASCINATION

_____

_____

_____

_____

_____

_____

_____

_____

_____

_____

_____

_____

Answer on page 233

Rockin' Ray Maze

This stingray is looking for a meal. Help the stingray get to the fish at the end of the maze.

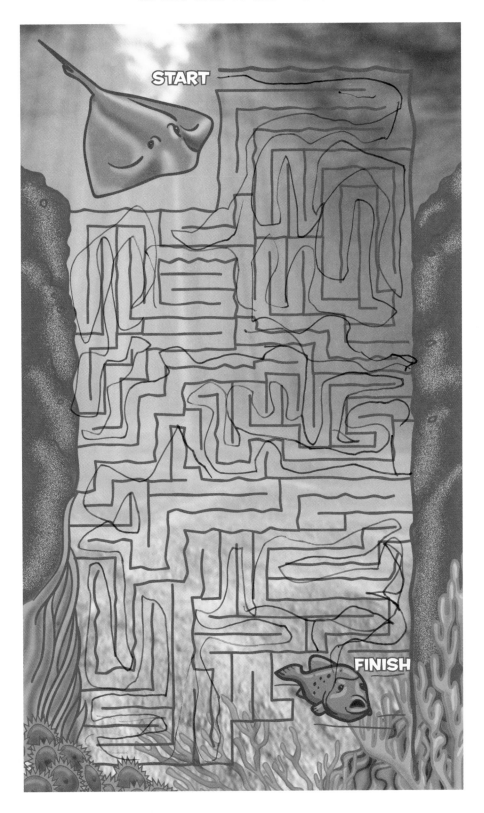

Trucks

Search, find, and circle these **10** things.

CHICKENS (3)   TOTEM POLE   TEAPOT
FOX   MUMMY   LIGHTHOUSE
DUMBBELL   MAGNET   ROBOT
                            MICE (2)

Answer on page 233

Poetic Puzzle

Solve this rebus puzzle to learn the name of a great American poet.

E + 🥛 − K + Y

D + 🧊 − E + 👑

− G + S + 1 − E

_ _ _ _ _ _ _

_ _ _ _ _ _ _ _

11

Lazy Sunday

Find **two sets of two objects** that rhyme with each other.

Answer on page 234

State Capitals

Put the capital that goes with each state in the crossword below.

across

1 OREGON — Salem

2 WEST VIRGINIA — Charston

3 IDAHO — Boise

4 New Jersey — Trenton

5 Rhode Island — Providence

DOWN

1 New Mexico — Santa Fe

6 Wisconsin — Madison

7 TENNESSEE — Nashville

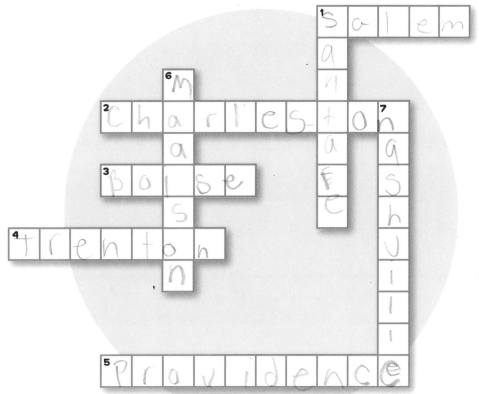

1 Salem
2 Charleston
3 Boise
4 Trenton
5 Providence
6 Madison
7 Nashville

Answer on page 234

Bust-a-Beat

Find 10 differences between the picture on the left and the one on the right.

Word Scramble

Unscramble each of these words using the clues.

RBID
(Likes to fly)

Bird

NUJE
(Summer month)

June

CEID
(Number game)

Dice

TCHAW
(Tells time)

watch

Answer on page 235

Fishing

Find these words that have to do with fishing in this word search.
Look up, down, backward, forward, and diagonally.

CAST
ROD
BAIT
CATFISH
WORM

CLEARWATER
LAKE
BOAT
FLY
REEL

```
U O S D B U V W N E W D V M
Z B R W K G C T E W T P H M
X C F E C G A Q A Y T R C M
X I A R E F S U S O R D C I
G T E T C L T N G X B P G X
F M A D F M X K M J R L Y J
Y J K B P I H H K R A G W N
W T I R L B S L P K O U A M
F O P U A E C H E Z S W D S
D Z A I T C F H Y E I G C O
G M T T G L B X G K J L Y T
Q V Z U Y V D O R U H L C N
D D R E T A W R A E L C S Q
B J Y G W D V C P Y I A X N
```

17

Where Am I?

Use the clues below to complete this crossword puzzle.

ACROSS
3 Circling
5 Hidden in back of
6 In the middle
7 Beneath

DOWN
1 Not indoors
2 Enter the building
4 Above
6 Next to

Answer on page 235

Decode-a-Message

Use the code key below to find a message that is considered an artistic intrument

A=3	D=9	N=10	R=2
B=11	E=1	O=8	Y=4
C=6	L=5	P=7	

__ __ __   __ __ __ __ __ __
2 1 9   6 2 3 4 8 10

Word Game

Look at the pictures below. Figure out what phrase uses these words and fill it in on the lines below.

___ ___ ___   ___ ___ ___ ___

___ ___ ___   ___ ___ ___ ___ ___   ___ ___ ___ .

Answer on page 236

Celebration

Can you make **25** words or more from the following word?

CELEBRATION

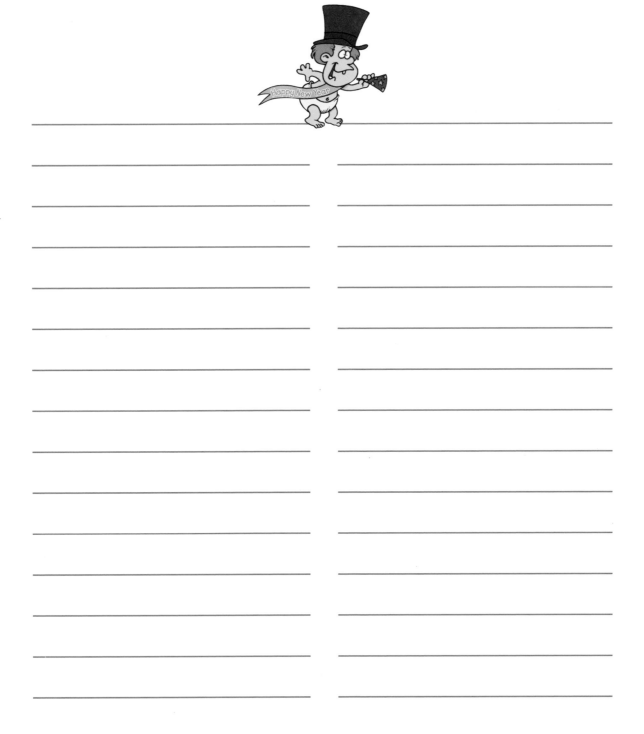

_____

_____   _____

_____   _____

_____   _____

_____   _____

_____   _____

_____   _____

_____   _____

_____   _____

_____   _____

_____   _____

_____   _____

_____   _____

21

Answer on page 236

Sudoku

Fill in the empty squares so that each row, column, and square box contains the numbers **1-9** only once.

4		3	6		8		2	9
		1	5				4	
9	8	7			2	1	6	5
3	9		8				7	
		6	9	2	3	5	8	
1			4	7	5		3	6
			7			6		4
8	1	4						
6	7	9	1	3	4			8

Answer on page 236

Ballerina

Use the pictures below to complete this crossword puzzle.

Answer on page 236

Slippery Stuff

Solve this rebus puzzle to find something fruity that you shouldn't eat.

− R − CH +   − H

− D +   − C − R +

− PPERS +   − E

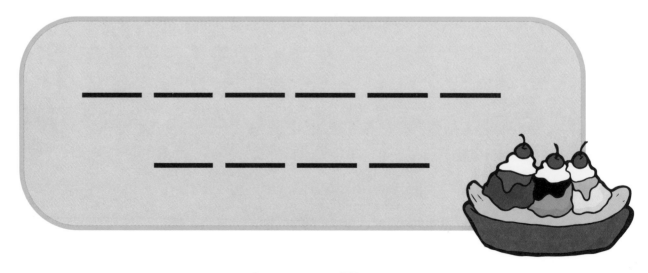

― ― ― ― ― ―

― ― ― ―

Creative Puzzle

Look at the pictures below. Figure out what phrase uses these words and fill it in on the lines below.

,

___ ___ ___ ___

___ ___ ___ ___ ___ .

Take a Trip

Use the clues below to complete this crossword puzzle.

ACROSS

1 You need these for the plane or train
5 Things to remember your trip by
6 Where to eat on a trip
8 Reference for info
9 Pack this up with clothes
10 Book in advance

DOWN

2 Snap those pictures
3 Mail these to your friends
4 Best seats on the plane
7 Leads you in a new place

Answer on page 237

Sudoku

Fill in the empty squares so that each row, column, and square box contains the numbers 1-9 only once.

3					4			6
2		7						9
8								
			7	2				
					3	1		8
				5		6	3	
		8			5			
	2				8	9	1	
9	1		6			7		

27

Strike Out

Search, find, and circle these **10** things.

BANANA PEELS (3)
BASKETBALL
CLOWN

DUCK
MOUSE
ROLLER SKATES
HAMBURGER

YO-YO
BONE
APPLE CORE

Answer on page 238

Word Scramble

Unscramble each of these words using the clues.

ILDAGFRUE
(Water rescue)

_ _ _ _ _ _ _ _ _

IMEETTSLO
(Christmas leaves hung in doorway)

_ _ _ _ _ _ _ _ _

SGNATYM
(Athlete)

_ _ _ _ _ _ _

NUUAMT
(Season)

_ _ _ _ _ _

AUMERSETPKR
(Food source)

_ _ _ _ _ _ _ _ _ _ _

EAMDMRI
(Fishy person)

_ _ _ _ _ _ _

AAGORKON
(Animal)

_ _ _ _ _ _ _ _

ALANSAG
(Food)

_ _ _ _ _ _ _

29

Answer on page 238

Tennis

Find these words that have to do with tennis in this word search.
Look up, down, backward, forward, and diagonally.

Love
Doubles
Volley
Fault
Sidelines

Backhand
Serve
Forehand
Ball
Point

I Z X M S B A C K H A N D V
D Y U C U I B L G N Z B L F
D J H R Q D D A L P T D D O
E O G Y D U Q E L W N G A R
O Y U A A H I T L L J L X E
E N C B G C C L G I E U P H
M B G E L B X U C H N Y S A
C L V M R E A A I K E E J N
G M X O E D S F Y Y A B S D
U S N M D T P M B A W Y V M
E A D E D N N T S E R V E O
M M D A V Q R I V G A L Z L
P M Q E Y O H V O L L E Y V
Q H Q O F S L U J P Y E H R

30

Answer on page 238

Lucky Number Three

Going from **Start** to **Finish**, choose the path
made up of the number **3** only.

Start

3	2	4	4	2
3	1	8	7	6
3	3	1	5	8
2	3	1	6	9
7	3	6	8	7
9	3	3	3	3

Finish

31

Rescue Vehicles

Based on the **problem** below, determine the appropriate rescue vehicle. Use the clues below to complete this crossword puzzle.

ACROSS
1 Broken leg
2 House fire
3 Search and rescue

DOWN
4 Burglar
5 Sea distress

Answer on page 239

Decode-a-Riddle

Use the code key below to find something that you would cook in your home.

A=5	E=6	I=2	M=3	S=4
C=11	G=13	K=7	N=12	U=14
D=1	H=9	L=8	P=10	

11	9	2	11	7	6	12	5	12	1

1	14	3	10	8	2	12	13	4

33

Answer on page 239

Double Octopuses

Can you find the two pictures that are exactly alike?

Answer on page 239

A Balanced Diet

Can you make **25** words or more from the following phrase?

A BALANCED DIET

_____ _____

_____ _____

_____ _____

_____ _____

_____ _____

_____ _____

_____ _____

_____ _____

_____ _____

_____ _____

_____ _____

_____ _____

Odd Birthday Maze

Guide this boy to the birthday cake by choosing the path made of **ODD** numbers only. You can only go **UP**, **DOWN**, and **ACROSS**—not diagonally.

Start

5	7	10	16	4	12
11	2	13	8	11	23
3	14	7	21	8	3
21	1	3	25	2	5
6	20	18	15	8	4
2	12	6	5	7	9
4	19	3	17	6	2
10	1	12	22	28	14
2	21	5	13	10	16
6	17	4	19	12	9
3	5	8	27	11	5

Finish

Answer on page 240

Holiday Time

Put the color of each holiday in the crossword below.

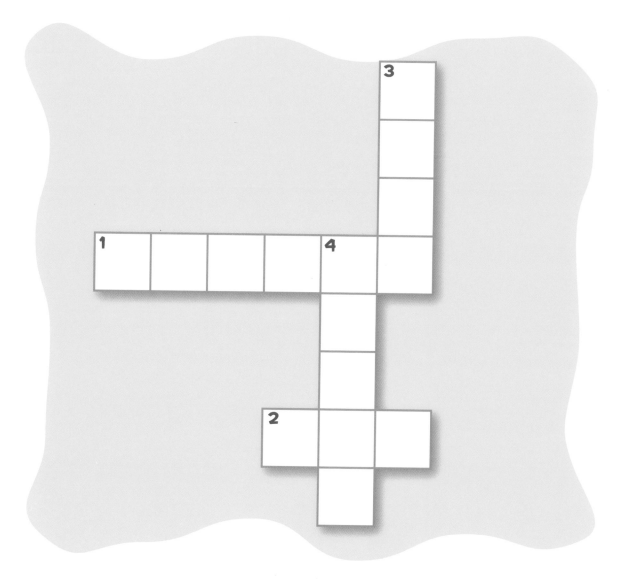

Answer on page 240

Super Singer

Solve this rebus puzzle to find someone talented and famous.

_ _ _ _

_ _ _ _

Hardware Store

Find **two sets of two objects** that rhyme with each other.

Pumpkin Harvest

Find 10 differences between the picture on the left and the one on the right.

Answer on page 241

U.S. Cities

Put the city of each attraction in the crossword puzzle below.

ACROSS
2 The White House
3 Hollywood
5 Mile High City
7 Golden Gate Bridge
8 Paul Revere

DOWN
1 Liberty Bell
4 Sears Tower
6 Empire State Building

Answer on page 241

Word Scramble

Unscramble each of these words using the clues.

REFLWO
(Blooming plant)

_ _ _ _ _ _

LDSALA
(Texas city)

_ _ _ _ _ _

GLUJEN
(Land of thick vegetation)

_ _ _ _ _ _

HTEGI
(Not seven or nine)

_ _ _ _ _

LETBLA
(Type of dance)

_ _ _ _ _ _

TROAC
(Pretending professional)

_ _ _ _ _

43

Tools

Find these types of tools in this word search. Look up, down, backward, forward, and diagonally.

SCREWDRIVER

CUTTER   MALLET

DRILL   WRENCH   SCRAPER

SAW   SANDER   HAMMER   AXE

S	S	D	F	M	R	U	I	Z	H	T	R	P	Y
T	C	I	R	E	P	A	R	C	S	W	A	S	Z
T	T	R	I	B	Y	R	M	I	I	F	Z	K	E
E	B	X	E	D	W	H	I	O	X	X	J	Q	D
L	J	A	T	W	J	R	H	A	M	M	E	R	B
L	L	H	X	H	D	S	E	L	A	N	Z	V	J
A	R	J	F	E	A	R	L	N	O	M	V	X	T
M	Y	M	O	N	V	I	I	U	C	B	J	M	L
W	O	U	D	R	R	Q	G	V	X	H	C	M	V
S	Z	E	H	D	Q	M	Y	H	E	U	P	W	R
P	R	I	V	R	P	S	H	W	T	R	K	W	T
K	D	S	I	D	C	E	H	T	F	K	Z	Q	F
S	F	G	E	G	D	U	E	K	Y	Y	X	X	M
D	D	U	X	A	C	R	D	Y	M	J	B	A	Y

Answer on page 242

Running Errands

This woman has one more errand to run, but her daughter keeps trying to tell her something. What's on the little girl's mind? Cross out the word "mom" wherever it appears to find out what she is trying to say.

**IMOMMOMNMOMEMOMEMOM
DMOMMOMTOMOMGOMOM
MOMTOMOMTMOMHMOMMOM
EMOMPMOMOMOMTMOMTMOMY!**

— —

— — — — —

— — —

— — —

— — —

— — — — —

— — — — — !

Summer Fun

Search, find, and circle these **10** things.

BOOK
SHOVEL
SAILOR

KITE
ALLIGATOR
COWBOY
ELEPHANT

MERMAID
BONE
MARSHMALLOW

Answer on page 242

Decode-a-Riddle

Use the code key below to decode and solve this riddle.

1=A	8=H	15=O	22=V
2=B	9=I	16=P	23=W
3=C	10=J	17=Q	24=X
4=D	11=K	18=R	25=Y
5=E	12=L	19=S	26=Z
6=F	13=M	20=T	
7=G	14=N	21=U	

23 8 1 20   3 1 14

25 15 21   11 5 5 16

1 6 20 5 18   25 15 21

7 9 22 5   9 20   20 15

19 15 13 5 15 14 5   5 12 19 5 **?**

25 15 21 18   23 15 18 4

Double Bananas

Can you find the two pictures that are exactly alike?

Answer on page 243

Agriculture

Can you make **25** words or more from the following word?

AGRICULTURE

_____   _____

_____   _____

_____   _____

_____   _____

_____   _____

_____   _____

_____   _____

_____   _____

_____   _____

_____   _____

_____   _____

_____   _____

Answer on page 243

Shark Maze

Help the leopard shark get back to the sea floor. Make sure to avoid the tiger shark, which might just make the leopard shark its dinner!

Answer on page 243

Animals

Use the pictures below to complete this crossword puzzle.

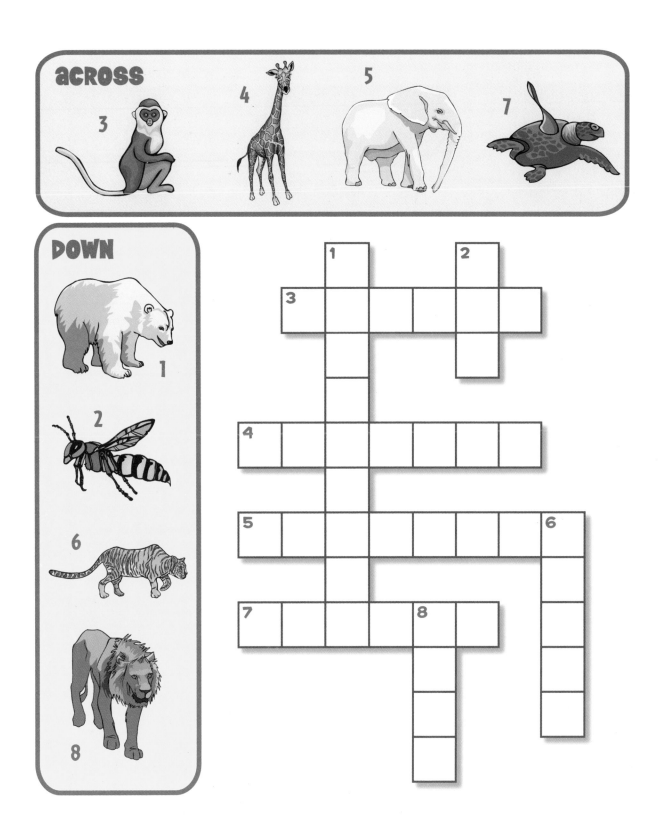

Answer on page 243

Camera Parts

Find these camera parts in the word search.
Look up, down, backward, forward, and diagonally.

FILM	BATTERIES
LENS	STRAP
SHUTTER	BODY
MOUNT	LEVER
FLASH	VIEWFINDER

```
S  B  P  R  R  O  F  P  A  H  Z  Z  H
N  H  A  D  C  O  I  U  D  X  W  O  P
X  R  O  T  F  O  L  F  G  E  L  S  I
T  P  E  L  T  K  M  A  K  R  P  H  M
X  P  E  D  Z  E  Z  M  E  L  S  X  Q
S  N  I  D  N  R  R  T  X  A  A  I  M
S  O  C  W  K  I  T  I  L  A  W  R  O
Y  D  V  L  R  U  F  F  E  Y  V  E  U
X  D  S  V  H  U  X  W  H  S  M  V  N
Y  X  O  S  P  P  Q  Y  E  U  B  E  T
B  A  Q  B  M  C  R  L  G  I  A  L  O
M  V  T  F  E  Q  Z  S  T  G  V  O  H
C  L  K  O  S  T  R  A  P  O  W  D  Q
```

Answer on page 244

Team Time

Use the clues below to complete this crossword puzzle.

ACROSS
- 3 Oakland baseball team
- 6 Atlanta hockey team
- 8 Cleveland basketball team
- 9 St. Louis baseball team
- 10 LA baseball team

DOWN
- 1 New York football team
- 2 Toronto hockey team
- 4 Dallas football team
- 5 Boston basketball team
- 7 New England football team

53

Wonderful Wizards

Search, find, and circle these **10** things.

ALIEN
CANDY CANE
COW

FLYING PIG
ICE-CREAM CONE
OWLS (7)
SANTA CLAUS

SOCCER BALL
SPIDERS (6)
TENNIS RACKET

Answer on page 244

Sudoku

Fill in the empty squares so that each row, column, and square box contains the numbers **1-9** only once.

4		9	3	7		8	5	6
		8	4					3
	7	3			8	2		4
2		6		5		3		
7		1	2	4	3	5		8
5		4		8		9		2
3				9			8	5
8		7	6			4		
9	4	5		1	2	6		7

Answer on page 244

Sticky Stuff

Solve this rebus puzzle to find the name of a delicious lunch.

Answer on page 245

Word Scramble

Unscramble each of these words using the clues.

TRENASTUAR
(Eating place)

_ _ _ _ _ _ _ _ _ _

CTYDNRIIAO
(Word describer)

_ _ _ _ _ _ _ _ _ _

RHCYISMTE
(Class subject)

_ _ _ _ _ _ _ _ _

RELIOPCHET
(Aircraft)

_ _ _ _ _ _ _ _ _ _

RPNEAAIL
(Sky coach)

_ _ _ _ _ _ _ _

LABLSBAE
(Throwing game)

_ _ _ _ _ _ _ _

SMULCE
(Under your skin)

_ _ _ _ _ _

OOIUYSLLQ
(Singly speaking)

_ _ _ _ _ _ _ _ _

Types of Dance

Find these types of dance in this word search. Look up, down, backward, forward, and diagonally.

BALLROOM   BALLET
FOLK   TANGO
MODERN   JAZZ
POLKA   TAP
SALSA   SQUARE

```
E Q M F E P Y D Q E G J R Q
B R Y S O T S J Y D Q U U Q
J V A L J X U A F B Q F K M
R N K U E C Y J L R G M D Q
Z A E E Q C H B K S R C Q N
T V J X I S T E L L A B G L
C A N U C K Y S S R O M R O
X R P R Q O C J W J O F W E
I X R P E X W N P O L O L L
Y N O B U D Q B R J U G T X
A D A H K S O L U V P N A N
O C G L T D L M Z Z A J N J
Y K K N P A S N N O V R G A
C G L D B D E H I W G E O J
```

Word Game

Look at the letters in the box below. Figure out what phrase about singing includes "GIG" and fill it in the lines below.

GIGINGIG

__ __ __ __ __ __ __ __ __

__ __ __ __

Answer on page 245

Yummy!

Use the clues below to complete this crossword puzzle.

aCROSS

4 Fresh and natural
6 Eat it at your birthday party
7 Frozen sweet treat
9 Thick and chocolaty
10 Liquid ice-cream drink

DOWN

1 Baked chocolate squares
2 Apple, pumpkin, chocolate cream
3 Lots in a box
5 Soft and sweet, chocolate or butterscotch
8 Drink it with cookies

60

Decode-a-Message

Use the code key below to find a message that has to do with dreaming.

A=2 H=16 O=13 T=3
C=12 I=7 P=5 U=8
D=4 M=15 R=6 W=14
E=10 N=9 S=11 Y=1

$\overline{14}$ $\overline{16}$ $\overline{10}$ $\overline{9}$ $\overline{1}$ $\overline{13}$ $\overline{8}$ $\overline{14}$ $\overline{7}$ $\overline{11}$ $\overline{16}$

$\overline{8}$ $\overline{5}$ $\overline{13}$ $\overline{9}$ $\overline{2}$ $\overline{11}$ $\overline{3}$ $\overline{2}$ $\overline{6}$'

$\overline{1}$ $\overline{13}$ $\overline{8}$ $\overline{6}$ $\overline{4}$ $\overline{6}$ $\overline{10}$ $\overline{2}$ $\overline{15}$ $\overline{11}$

$\overline{12}$ $\overline{13}$ $\overline{15}$ $\overline{10}$ $\overline{3}$ $\overline{6}$ $\overline{8}$ $\overline{10}$.

61

Answer on page 246

Double Ladybugs

Can you find the two pictures that are exactly alike?

Answer on page 246

Engagement

Can you make **25** words or more from the following word?

ENGAGEMENT

Even Bear Maze

Guide this bear to the honeycomb by choosing the correct path made of **EVEN** numbers only.

Answer on page 247

Vehicle Sounds

Put the sounds associated with each picture in the crossword puzzle below.

Answer on page 247

Mythical Animal

Solve this rebus puzzle to find the name of a mythical animal.

−CYCLE +  −

−RAY − ON + −

−A − MENT

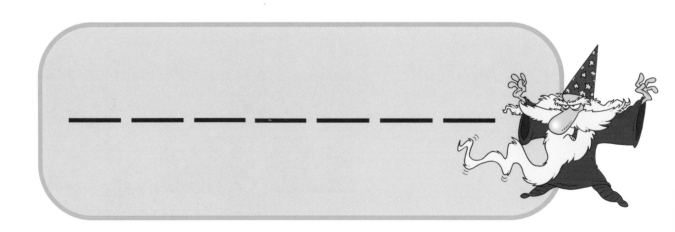

— — — — — — —

66

Double Dinosaurs

Can you find the two pictures that are exactly alike?

Safari Trip

Find **10** differences between the picture on the left and the one on the right.

Answer on page 248

Airplanes

Search, find, and circle these 10 things.

APPLE
BASEBALL
BEACH BALL

BIRDS' NEST
CLOWNS (5)
FISHBOWL
ROBOT

TOAST
TOOTHBRUSH
ZEBRA

Answer on page 248

Word Scramble

Unscramble each of these words using the clues.

TNCFORON
(Face up against)

_ _ _ _ _ _ _ _

LEGRAYL
(Place where art is shown)

_ _ _ _ _ _ _

TANGINMAIOI
(Creative thinking)

_ _ _ _ _ _ _ _ _ _ _

CATINTRATO
(Appeal, pull)

_ _ _ _ _ _ _ _ _ _

CIVDEENE
(Proof)

_ _ _ _ _ _ _ _

DUNHATE
(Filled with ghosts)

_ _ _ _ _ _ _

GAGUNALE
(Word of a country)

_ _ _ _ _ _ _ _

JASMAAP
(What you wear to bed)

_ _ _ _ _ _ _

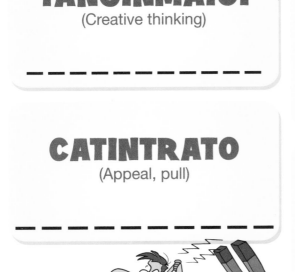

71

Fish

Find these types of fish in this word search. Look up, down, backward, forward, and diagonally.

Shark   Barracuda
Eel   Goldfish
Salmon   Haddock
Bass   Flounder
Sunfish   Anglerfish

I	P	L	A	N	E	U	O	R	Q	J	G	F	Q
F	L	D	L	A	B	R	N	R	B	O	H	K	C
F	H	W	T	Q	Y	K	C	F	L	U	S	F	S
N	I	Q	E	E	L	K	W	D	R	A	I	H	S
Y	K	R	A	H	S	I	F	F	D	V	F	H	A
R	S	S	H	H	Z	I	X	U	O	H	R	K	B
C	L	A	C	S	S	Z	C	N	G	O	E	C	C
K	Y	L	Z	H	I	A	K	D	N	U	L	O	E
Y	A	M	U	S	R	F	Y	S	D	D	G	D	Q
U	J	O	H	R	L	S	N	Q	A	J	N	D	Y
D	U	N	A	C	S	S	X	U	Z	V	A	A	F
X	H	B	Y	X	E	U	Y	R	S	O	A	H	K
J	F	L	O	U	N	D	E	R	S	C	A	C	H
L	H	T	Q	S	K	V	H	A	S	G	L	D	V

Answer on page 249

Sudoku

Fill in the empty squares so that each row, column, and square box contains the numbers 1-9 only once.

8		5			6	2	4	
1	7		5		4			8
	6	3	1	2		9	5	
2		1	4			8		
	3			5	7		2	
		6			9	5		4
	1	8	3		5			2
		7		8		6		3
3		9	6	4			8	

73

Answer on page 249

Thirsty

Use the clues below to complete this crossword puzzle.

ACROSS
4 Clear and simple
5 Grind and brew
6 Sweet and bubbly
8 To gulp down

DOWN
1 Brewed from a bag
2 From fruit
3 Made with lemons
7 Good with chocolate

Answer on page 249

Decode-a-Message

Use the code key below to find a message that has to do with a wintry day.

A=4	H=3	T=2
C=1	O=5	

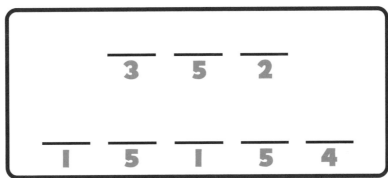

$\overline{}$ $\overline{}$ $\overline{}$
  3   5   2

$\overline{}$ $\overline{}$ $\overline{}$ $\overline{}$ $\overline{}$
  1   5   1   5   4

Answer on page 249

Word Game

Look at the pictures below. Figure out what phrase uses these words and fill it in on the lines below.

___ ___   ___ ___ ___

___ ___ ___ ___ ___   ___ ___   ___ ___ ___ ___

___ ___ ___ ___ ___ ___ ___ ___ ___

Answer on page 250

Burglarize

Can you make **25** words or more from the following word?

BURGLARIZE

Answer on page 250

Lucky Number Two

Going from **Start** to **Finish**, choose the path
made up of the number **2** only.

Start

2	2	3	7	3
5	2	2	5	5
6	9	2	8	8
7	7	2	7	9
8	5	2	2	7
9	4	3	2	2

Finish

Answer on page 250

State Capitals

Put the capital that goes with each state in the crossword puzzle below.

Answer on page 250

Wet Adventure

Solve this rebus puzzle to find a neat place to explore.

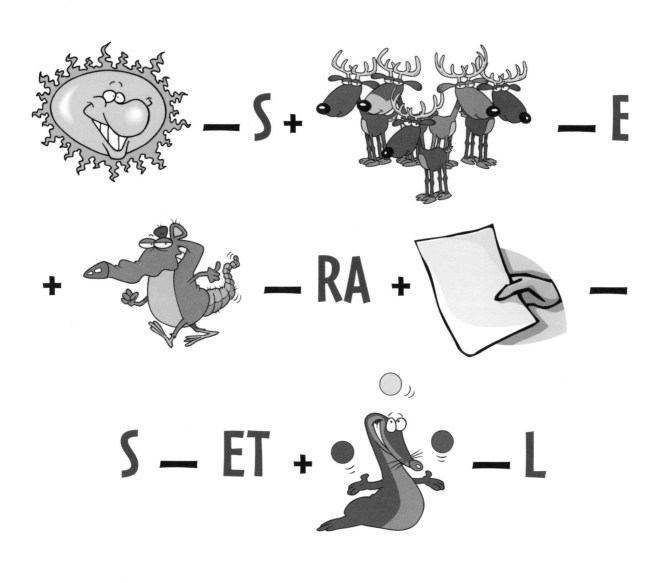

Answer on page 251

Opposites Attract

List the opposite of each word in the spaces below. Then read down the column to learn the opposite of **OUTSIDE**.

1) DARK _____ 4) SMALL _____

2) OLD _____ 5) SHALLOW _____

3) ENEMIES _____ 6) DRY _____

Types of Bears

Find these types of bears in the word search.
Look up, down, backward, forward, and diagonally.

Black   **Panda**   **Polar**
Cinnamon   **Sloth**
Gobi   **Spectacled**
Brown   **Sun**
Red   **Grizzly**

```
P H R N B I L X X O X L M O Q
X N A T O Z S U O H W K K J A
G E S L I M L D V N C S A H L
N I S G S Q A V Q F N K U H A
Q C B B A P M N W I E D T N D
M F R O L O E E N E F O C Y K
Y U A L G A O C A I L Z C E Y
Y Y L E X S C X T S C J V X S
T Z O K C D H K T A C X I D T
O S P P K C Q K A F C S K Q F
Q N G D A V N Q M Q D L M U R
L J L H F N B R O W N D E Z S
L X R P O N D L O C Q P I D D
C B D K A A E A B T C M U T H
Y N E R E D A G R I Z Z L Y U
```

Answer on page 251

Sudoku

Fill in the empty squares so that each row, column, and square box contains the numbers **1-9** only once.

						2		
8		3	2				9	
	4		9	7		6		
			7		9			1
	9	6	3		1	7	8	
3			5		6			
		5		3	4		1	
	6				2	4		3
		8						

83

Carnival Fun

Search, find, and circle these **10** things.

BASEBALL GLOVE ~~FLAG~~ ~~SKATEBOARDS (2)~~
~~BOWLING BALL~~ ~~LION~~ ~~UNICYCLE~~
~~COTTON CANDY~~ ROBOT ~~FRANKENSTEIN~~
~~JACK-O'-LANTERN~~

Answer on page 252

Word Scramble

Unscramble each of these words using the clues.

TEGILINNS
(Paying attention to)

__ __ __ __ __ __ __ __ __

YERVNOEE
(All the people)

__ __ __ __ __ __ __ __

RATHEFES
(On a bird)

__ __ __ __ __ __ __ __

GIPVIRLEE
(Advantage, special treatment)

__ __ __ __ __ __ __ __ __

GALMENGI
(Shining)

__ __ __ __ __ __ __ __

SELNERLETS
(Persistant, not stopping)

__ __ __ __ __ __ __ __ __ __

PIWRESH
(Speak softly)

__ __ __ __ __ __ __

KRADYABC
(Behind the house)

__ __ __ __ __ __ __ __

85

Bicycle Ride

Find these words that have to do with a bicycle in this word search.
Look up, down, backward, forward, and diagonally.

Helmet   Pump
Chain   Lock
Gloves   Incline
Shoes   Bell
Tire   Handlebar

Q	H	S	Y	D	S	J	N	E	R	I	T	I	M
R	B	H	H	V	E	U	C	P	F	S	U	C	E
A	E	O	D	U	S	E	B	D	U	K	J	W	H
J	L	E	G	H	C	E	H	Z	L	P	R	S	G
U	L	S	G	A	I	E	V	E	P	S	L	X	Z
R	B	X	M	K	N	O	F	O	L	W	J	M	L
A	P	M	U	P	C	B	A	M	L	M	F	U	V
B	D	D	V	F	L	Y	C	K	C	G	E	I	C
E	E	K	B	X	I	F	B	Y	D	M	H	T	J
L	N	L	F	M	N	J	Y	E	D	E	C	H	H
D	K	H	C	I	E	B	E	A	Z	P	W	F	X
N	P	F	A	G	Z	I	C	P	T	D	K	D	N
A	B	H	B	P	B	F	Q	Z	L	O	C	K	E
H	C	H	V	U	K	O	I	R	Z	J	P	P	L

86

Answer on page 252

Let's Build

Unscramble these construction vehicles on the blanks below and then place them in the crossword puzzle.

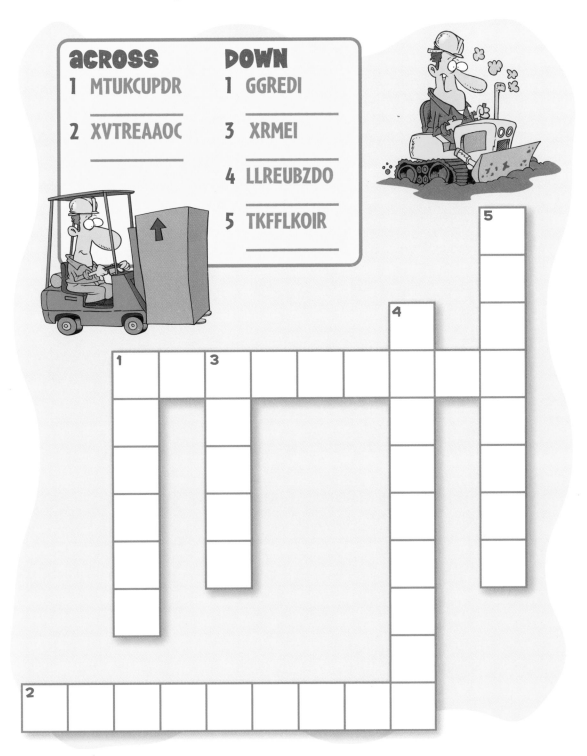

across

1 MTUKCUPDR
_____

2 XVTREAAOC
_____

DOWN

1 GGREDI
_____

3 XRMEI
_____

4 LLREUBZDO
_____

5 TKFFLKOIR
_____

Game Time

Use the clues below to complete this crossword puzzle.

across
1 Kings and queens
5 Toss a ball back and forth
8 Hand off the baton
9 Card game with bids
10 Three water birds
11 Two hands, no tackling

DOWN
2 Find the missing item
3 Ready or not, here I come
4 Spin the rope, jump
5 Jump my piece
6 You're it!
7 Small glass balls

Answer on page 253

Lunchtime

Use the code key below to find a something that has to do with a lunchbreak.

A=8	F=16	K=9	R=10
B=14	G=1	M=15	S=6
C=11	H=5	N=7	T=12
E=4	I=2	O=3	W=13

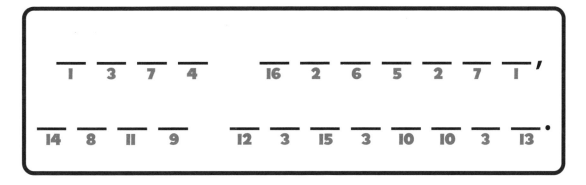

__ __ __ __   __ __ __ __ __ __ __'
 1 3 7 4   16 2 6 5 2 7 1

__ __ __ __   __ __ __ __ __ __ __ __.
14 8 11 9   12 3 15 3 10 10 3 13

89

Double Kites

Can you find the two pictures that are exactly alike?

Answer on page 253

Anatomical

Can you make **25** words or more from the following word?

ANATOMICAL

Odd House Maze

Guide this woman back to her house by choosing the correct path made of **ODD** numbers only. You can only go **UP**, **DOWN**, and **ACROSS**—not diagonally.

1	6	4	8	2	1
2	1	3	12	1	4
10	4	17	3	13	21

Start ↓

8	12	3	2	9	12	3	9	11
4	16	9	10	11	8	9	2	3
12	7	5	8	9	1	5	4	7
9	2	9	3	10	3	4	1	10
1	3	10	15	7	19	5	3	7

8	4	17	4	2	9	8
5	6	12	13	10	5	5
5	9	15	7	3	17	2

Finish ←

Answer on page 254

Under the Sea

Use the pictures below to complete this crossword puzzle.

93

On the Go

Solve this rebus puzzle to find something you need when you travel.

Answer on page 254

Sudoku

Fill in the empty squares so that each row, column, and square box contains the numbers **1-9** only once.

2		9	5	8		7		6
6							5	
		5	6	4		9		2
	5	3	2			4		
9				5	4	6	1	
4	6		8	3	9			7
	9			7	2	3		
3	2	6		9				
5	7			6	8		9	1

95

Ice Hockey Game

Find **10** differences between the picture on the left and the one on the right.

Answer on page 255

Traveling Circus

Search, find, and circle these **10** things.

BALLOONS (14)　　**FIRE HYDRANT**　　**PARTY HAT**
BANJO　　**HAMBURGERS (2)**　　**PENGUIN**
CRICKET　　**MOUSE**　　**TURTLES (4)**
NECKTIE (3)

Answer on page 255

Word Scramble

Unscramble each of these words using the clues.

ACPEH
(Juicy summer fruit)

_ _ _ _ _

ROYRW
(To fret, be concerned)

_ _ _ _ _

SHUP
(To shove)

_ _ _ _

ARHI
(It's on your head)

_ _ _ _

POTS
(Halt, cease)

_ _ _ _

GTHIL
(Bright, glowing bulb)

_ _ _ _ _

PLHE
(Assist)

_ _ _ _

UHTTR
(Honestly)

_ _ _ _ _

99

Car Parts

Find these car parts in this word search. Look up, down, backward, forward, and diagonally.

Tailgate	Brakes
Bumper	Horn
Tire	Grille
Dashboard	Hubcap
Engine	Exhaust pipe

H W O B D K E N O E N N O K

R L B F U E R R R U B O B Y

V R D L K M L C I O D N C J

B Z E O E T P L U T H M Q E

X M F L W M G E B X T T F X

J K H T L P U R R O A V K H

Q O E U A I A Y U I W V W A

K N V Q B K R Q L F N U K U

V R R Q E C G G L Q R V A S

L U H S A D A N I M B Z W T

I U V G E T C P C X Z F Y P

F N B Z E D O E N I G N E I

S P J R J Y Q T M V G Z M P

S R D A S H B O A R D Z J E

100

Sudoku

Fill in the empty squares so that each row, column, and square box contains the numbers **1 - 9** only once.

	2				8	9		3
	9		3	6	4	8		
		8		9	1		7	
						3		1
4	7	9		3		5		
3			8		2		4	
8		3	6			4	9	7
					9			6
9	4				3		8	5

Answer on page 256

Authors

Write these famous authors' first names in the blanks below and then complete this crossword puzzle.

ACROSS
1 ___ Christian Anderson
2 ___ Kipling
3 ___ Dickens
4 ___ Shelley
5 ___ Austen

DOWN
1 ___ Melville
2 ___ Waldo Emerson
5 ___ London
6 ___ Carroll
7 ___ Hodgson Burnett

Answer on page 256

Decode-a-Riddle

Use the code key below to find something
that has to do with a little bambino.

A=4   I=8   S=2

B=1   M=9   T=5

E=6   O=3   Y=7

__ __ __ __
1 4 1 7

__ __ __ __ __ __ __
1 3 5 5 3 9 2

Answer on page 256

Double Aliens

Can you find the two pictures that are exactly alike?

Answer on page 257

Influenza

Can you make **25** words or more from the following word?

INFLUENZA

Shopping Time

Guide this man through this maze to the cashier by putting **1** to **36** in the correct order. You can only go **UP**, **DOWN**, and **ACROSS**—not diagonally.

Start

6	5	4	3	2	1
7	6	5	4	5	2
8	9	10	5	12	3
9	8	7	6	11	4
20	21	22	7	10	5
19	24	23	8	9	6
18	19	12	11	10	7
17	20	21	22	11	8

16	15	14	13	12	9	10	11	12
17	18	19	20	21	22	23	24	13
20	19	36	35	26	25	24	15	14

Finish

		34	33	32	25	26	27
		33	34	35	26	35	28
		32	35	28	27	30	29
		31	30	29	32	31	30
		32	33	34	35	32	31

Answer on page 257

I'm Hungry

Use the pictures below to complete this crossword puzzle.

107

Dangerous Weather

Solve this rebus puzzle to find out a sign of dangerous weather.

+ AST + ⬡ − I − G +

🃑 − C − R + O + 🛒 −

GON + R + 9 0 − ETY + G

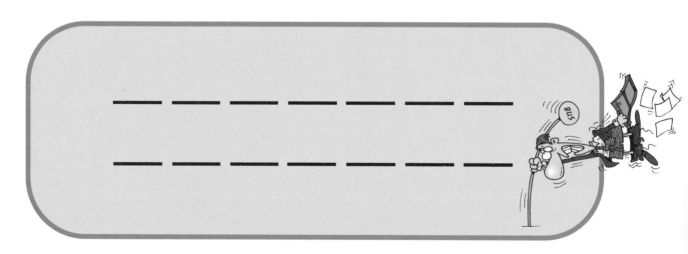

Answer on page 258

Class Schedule

Put the school subjects of each topic in the crossword puzzle below.

ACROSS
1 Latitude/ Longitude
2 Expressionism
3 Pythagorean Theorem

DOWN
4 Sonnet
5 War of 1812
6 Empirical Charts

Answer on page 258

Beach Time

Find these things that have to do with the beach in the word search. Look up, down, backword, forward, and diagonally.

Lotion   Swimsuit
Sand   Waves
Ocean   Shovel
Chair   Swimming
Umbrella   Surfing

W	A	G	V	U	M	B	R	E	L	L	A	W	A
O	R	N	A	Q	H	F	Y	T	S	S	U	M	Y
V	S	I	M	P	I	K	L	W	C	U	V	D	B
O	H	M	J	B	J	Q	I	F	E	M	R	J	U
Y	O	M	Y	I	A	M	Q	N	L	K	U	X	H
R	V	I	P	A	S	R	B	O	A	L	D	U	C
I	E	W	V	U	K	Y	T	T	B	E	M	C	P
A	L	S	I	Q	W	I	R	J	R	B	C	X	B
H	B	T	Z	X	O	A	N	D	P	B	Q	O	J
C	P	O	G	N	Q	R	V	X	N	P	T	W	R
B	X	R	G	K	M	P	L	E	K	A	T	Y	G
L	C	P	F	N	A	M	A	Q	S	U	S	Q	K
S	U	R	F	I	N	G	G	J	S	I	B	B	G
X	K	P	A	S	H	W	O	T	G	A	A	O	X

Answer on page 258

Sudoku

Fill in the empty squares so that each row, column, and square box contains the numbers **1**-**9** only once.

7				8		3		
	9		4		1			8
8		2		7				
3			8		9		7	2
	8			2		6	3	4
4						8		
		4			8	2		
						5		
6				5		4		3

Dino Paradise

Search, find, and circle these **10** things.

BABY CARRIAGE
BASKETBALL
BERET

CAKE
CHEESE
FEATHER
PAIL

POPCORN
SLIDE
VOLLEYBALLS (2)

Answer on page 259

Word Scramble

Unscramble each of these words using the clues.

VDOE
(Bird of peace)

_ _ _ _

HWOS
(Performance)

_ _ _ _

HCSOK
(Surprise, stun)

_ _ _ _ _

LADE
(Hand out cards)

_ _ _ _

KACP
(Put into a suitcase)

_ _ _ _

KRWO
(Do a job)

_ _ _ _

PLIF
(Turn over)

_ _ _ _

IJNO
(Become part of a club or team)

_ _ _ _

Answer on page 259

Types of Birds

Find these types of birds in this word search. Look up, down, backward, forward, and diagonally.

Mockingbird
Heron
Hummingbird
Shorebird
Bluebird

Wren
Sparrow
Woodpecker
Warbler
Duck

P	J	W	R	E	N	D	J	S	J	H	B	M	C
G	H	J	I	Q	Q	O	H	G	U	L	H	O	R
U	L	C	K	P	N	O	B	M	U	N	E	C	L
A	L	C	C	U	R	R	M	E	U	C	R	K	O
T	W	M	X	E	B	I	B	K	G	C	O	I	G
M	I	O	B	K	N	I	Z	C	H	L	N	N	E
R	S	I	O	G	R	Q	M	U	J	B	N	G	N
I	R	P	B	D	X	C	S	D	R	K	T	B	C
D	M	I	A	A	P	J	R	S	A	Q	C	I	X
P	R	U	C	R	B	E	U	L	C	R	X	R	X
D	T	B	G	J	R	S	C	U	F	O	B	D	T
Y	W	X	R	D	A	O	R	K	D	T	C	J	L
Y	O	R	E	L	Q	J	W	M	E	S	O	X	D
N	G	M	R	E	L	B	R	A	W	R	T	V	K

Answer on page 259

Militaristic

Unscramble these things that have to do with the military on the blanks below and then place them in this crossword puzzle.

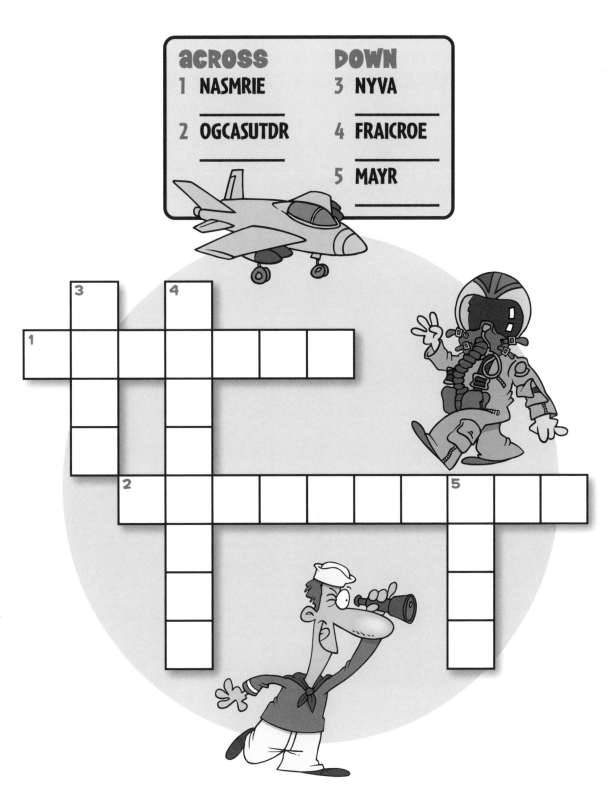

ACROSS

1 NASMRIE
_____

2 OGCASUTDR
_____

DOWN

3 NYVA
_____

4 FRAICROE
_____

5 MAYR
_____

Musical Instruments

Use the clues below to complete this crossword puzzle.

across

4 Long, silver woodwind instrument
5 Woodwind instrument that sounds like a duck
6 Jazz instrument with a double reed

DOWN

1 Biggest baritone brass instrument
2 Second largest, upright orchestra instrument
3 Highest-pitched band instrument

Answer on page 260

Decode-a-Message

Use the code key below to find something that has
to do with grooming.

A=2   G=1   M=3   O=6   T=5
D=7   H=4   N=10   R=11   W=9
E=12   I=8   Y=13

__4__ __2__ __8__ __11__   __5__ __6__ __7__ __2__ __13__'

__1__ __6__ __10__ __12__

__5__ __6__ __3__ __6__ __11__ __11__ __6__ __9__.

Answer on page 260

Double Skydivers

Can you find the two pictures that are exactly alike?

Answer on page 260

Veterinarian

Can you make **25** words or more from the following word?

VETERINARIAN

119

Answer on page 260

Even Plane Maze

Fly this plane to the runway by choosing the correct path made of **EVEN** numbers only. You can only go **UP**, **DOWN**, and **ACROSS**—not diagonally.

12	16	2	8	10	← Start
6	1	5	11	2	
4	22	18	3	13	
8	19	6	10	14	
7	16	22	9	20	
12	5	13	21	12	
4	8	16	2	6	
10	3	6	11	7	

Finish ←

Answer on page 261

What Time Is It?

Use the pictures below to complete this crossword puzzle.

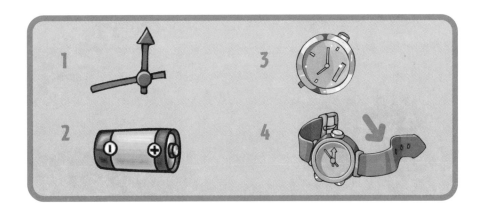

121

Fun For All

Solve this rebus puzzle to find out something that happens when you're having fun.

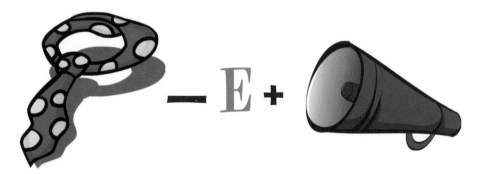 — E +

— GA — PHONE

+  — PPER + I + ES

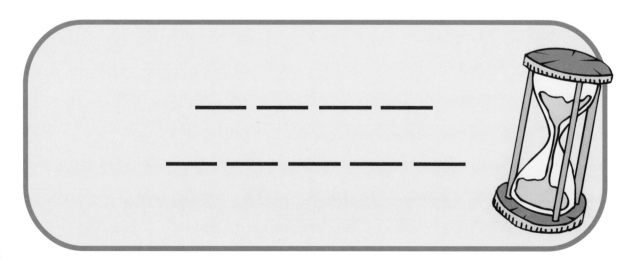

_ _ _ _ _
_ _ _ _ _

Double Apples

Can you find the two pictures that are exactly alike?

123

Answer on page 261

Pretty Peacocks

Find **10** differences between the picture on the left and the one on the right.

125

Answer on page 262

Pyramids

Search, find, and circle these **10** things.

ALIENS (2)   **DUCKS (2)**   **GINGERBREAD MAN**
BIRDS' NEST   **FIRE HYDRANT**   **PIE**
CHEERLEADER   **MONKEY**   **SNORKEL**
MAGNIFYING GLASS

Answer on page 262

Word Scramble

Unscramble each of these words using the clues.

VAERBEEG
(Thirst quencher)

_ _ _ _ _ _ _ _

REOEIHN
(Female hero)

_ _ _ _ _ _ _

YSYSEDO
(Epic journey)

_ _ _ _ _ _ _

BHRMAUEGR
(Goes with fries)

_ _ _ _ _ _ _ _ _

GIISHATNKGVN
(Holiday)

_ _ _ _ _ _ _ _ _ _ _ _

OEOTCSINRNVA
(Long chat)

_ _ _ _ _ _ _ _ _ _ _ _

ELADTOR
(Ballerina wear)

_ _ _ _ _ _ _

OGBIWLN
(Rolling game)

_ _ _ _ _ _ _

Answer on page 262

Healthy Food

Find these types of healthy food in this word search. Look up, down, backward, forward, and diagonally.

FRUIT	WHOLE GRAIN
VEGETABLES	RAISINS
BEANS	GRANOLA
FIBER	YOGURT
NUTS	CHICKEN

R A I S I N S K D V E Z M
Q R E B I F X O R S Y A X
S T O V F D G E T O L L V
N J F N E R F Q G Q W O E
A P Z I U H U U H H C N G
E Z W A X T R I O K U A E
B U B M D T S L T S R R T
G D W M Z W E D J G X G A
S S P G Y G N X S J T M B
G F J N R R R X T X N U L
G C S A P I Z B J M V W E
Q Y I C H I C K E N I D S
M N Y Q E K W I A C J O E

Answer on page 263

Sudoku

Fill in the empty squares so that each row, column, and square box contains the numbers 1-9 only once.

3	2	1	4		5		6	
6			2		1		5	
	7	5		8	6	2		4
		6	7			5		8
7	5				4			9
1		8	5		9	7		6
		7		3	8	4	9	
8			6		2	3		5
	4		9		7	6	8	1

Building a House

Use the clues below to complete this crossword puzzle.

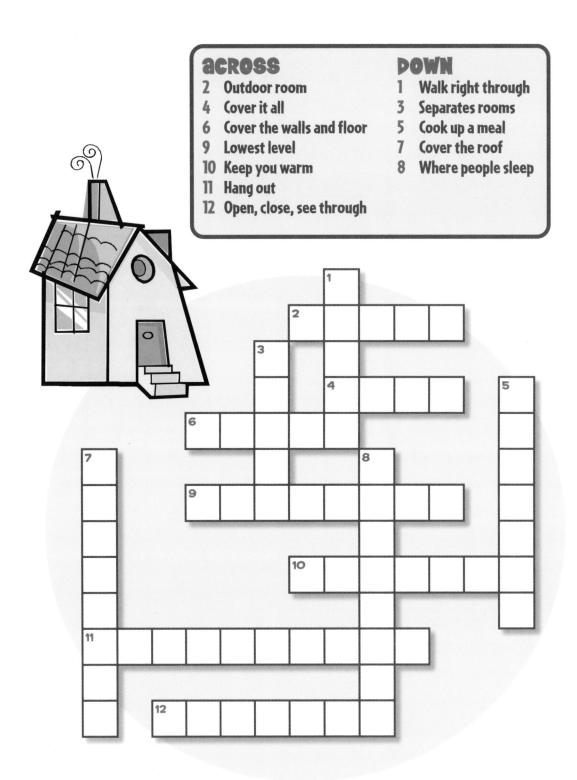

ACROSS
2 Outdoor room
4 Cover it all
6 Cover the walls and floor
9 Lowest level
10 Keep you warm
11 Hang out
12 Open, close, see through

DOWN
1 Walk right through
3 Separates rooms
5 Cook up a meal
7 Cover the roof
8 Where people sleep

Answer on page 263

Decode-a-Riddle

Use the key code below to decode and solve this riddle.

A=!   H=*   O=>   V=?
B=@   I=(P=[W=/
C=#   J=+   Q=]   X=\
D=$ K=)   R="   Y=}
E=%   L=;   S="   Z={
F=^   M=:   T='
G=&   N=<   U='

/ * ! ' (" ! <

> " ! < & ' ' ! < " ,

^ ! ? > " (' % ' > > ; ?

! : > <) % }

/ " % < # *

Animal Habitats

Draw a line between the animals in the first column that belong in the habitats in the second column.

Answer on page 264

Dinnertime

Can you make **25** words or more from the following word?

DINNERTIME

A-maze-ing Ray

This manta ray is looking for a meal. Help the manta ray get to the plankton at the end of the maze.

Answer on page 264

In the Cupboard

Use the pictures below to complete this crossword puzzle.

Name of a Leader

Solve this rebus puzzle to find out the name of a leader.

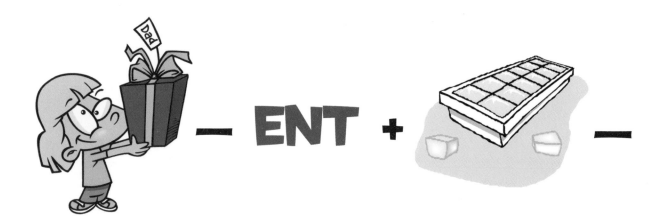

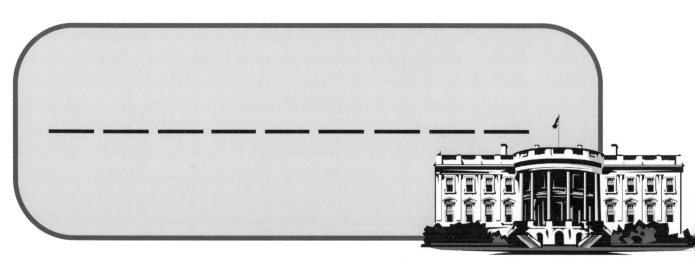

136

Answer on page 265

School Bus

Find **two sets of two objects** that rhyme with each other.

Answer on page 265

Track and Field

Find these things that have to do with track and field in the word search. Look up, down, backward, forward, and diagonally.

Running
Hurdle
Start
Finish
Crossbar

Endurance
Relay
Interval
Spikes
Training

O R D M I O C J L G K Y T E
T E I H Z N T K N N L W R J
U L U P C B T I X S X K W B
S A E D I O N E T Z M L H E
E Y A U J I B A R X R M V G
Y N T C A D R B P V H G L C
R Z D R L T S J R G A O I L
U L T U E L D R U H K L C T
N N N D R S P I K E S F J X
N L W T N A Y V X X J L W M
I E Z Z K S N F Q Y B D L V
N F I N I S H C H M K J A T
G M P A I O P D E R A M I N
N L R A B S S O R C U E E S

138

More State Capitals

Put the capital of each state in the crossword puzzle below.

ACROSS
2 Texas
6 Georgia
8 Oregon
10 Idaho

DOWN
1 Alaska
3 Kansas
4 Ohio
5 Michigan
7 New York
9 Delaware

139

Answer on page 265

Lemonade Stand

Search, find, and circle these **10** things.

FROG
GOPHERS (2)
PILLOW

FIRE HYDRANT
MICE (7)
OWL
PORCUPINE

GINGERBREAD MAN
SQUIRREL
UFO

Answer on page 266

Word Scramble

Unscramble each of these words using the clues.

SOGOE
(Bird)

_ _ _ _ _

YDINW
(Air moving)

_ _ _ _ _

TRAGUI
(Instrument)

_ _ _ _ _ _

JNUAC
(Spicy style)

_ _ _ _ _

BITRBA
(Twitchy animal)

_ _ _ _ _ _

EHUSO
(Dwelling)

_ _ _ _ _

Classic Books

Find these name of classic books in this word search. Look up, down, backward, forward, and diagonally.

Pinocchio
The Wizard of Oz
Little Women
Black Beauty
Treasure Island

A S Z Y H D U X E L O F D V D
Q L F J M K L K Y Y X G Z X N
Z K J P A B K N Z X K I U L A
B O N Z C X E Y H D P B T I L
U L F B Q V D G J T F C G T S
K D A O I H C C O N I P Y T I
T U P C D J H C Z M V U B L E
T T I L K R N J V O J A W E R
B B B I A B A T G Q X Q T W U
W P W Q F E E Z L P J W G O S
K H F K W A Z A I J R K K M A
C S R P A X K V U W O Q S E E
C M D B O Y T M J T E E T N R
H X F V O P Y K T R Y H W S T
F T A Z F I O W F Y Y I T U Q

Sudoku

Fill in the empty squares so that each row, column, and square box contains the numbers **1-9** only once.

8	4	2	9			6		
	1	9		8	6		3	4
6		3	7		4			2
3			5		2		9	6
	6							
9		5	6		1	3		
1	9		4		5	8		3
4		7	8	3		1	6	
5			1			2	4	9

143

Time to Laugh

Use the clues below to complete this crossword puzzle.

ACROSS
2 Little laugh
7 ____—____ who's there?
8 Silly questions and answers

DOWN
1 Show your teeth
3 Animated shows
4 In the circus
5 Stand-up guy
6 Tell me funny ones

Answer on page 267

Decode-a-Message

Use the code key below to find a message
that has to do with a cave.

A=6   G=10   N=1   T=4
D=2   H=3   O=7   U=11
E=8   I=5   R=14
F=13   L=12   S=9

END OF THE TUNNEL

$\overline{4}$ $\overline{3}$ $\overline{8}$ $\overline{14}$ $\overline{8}$ $\overline{5}$ $\overline{9}$ $\overline{6}$

$\overline{12}$ $\overline{5}$ $\overline{10}$ $\overline{3}$ $\overline{4}$ $\overline{6}$ $\overline{4}$ $\overline{4}$ $\overline{3}$ $\overline{8}$

$\overline{8}$ $\overline{1}$ $\overline{2}$ $\overline{7}$ $\overline{13}$ $\overline{4}$ $\overline{3}$ $\overline{8}$

$\overline{4}$ $\overline{11}$ $\overline{1}$ $\overline{1}$ $\overline{8}$ $\overline{12}$.

145

Double Cats

Can you find the two pictures that are exactly alike?

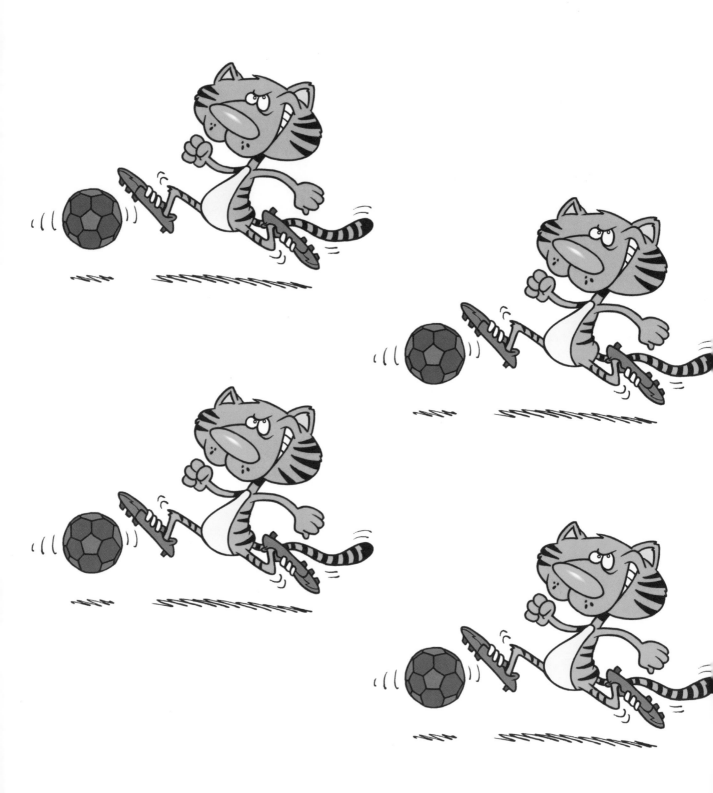

Answer on page 267

Alphabet Soup

Can you make **25** words or more from the following phrase?

ALPHABET SOUP

Lucky Number 18

Going from **Start** to **Finish**, choose the path
made up of the number **18** only.

Start

18	12	13	17	13
18	12	12	15	15
18	18	12	14	13
17	18	18	17	19
14	15	18	12	17
19	13	18	18	18

Finish

Answer on page 268

Sudoku

Fill in the empty squares so that each row, column, and square box contains the numbers 1 - 4 only once.

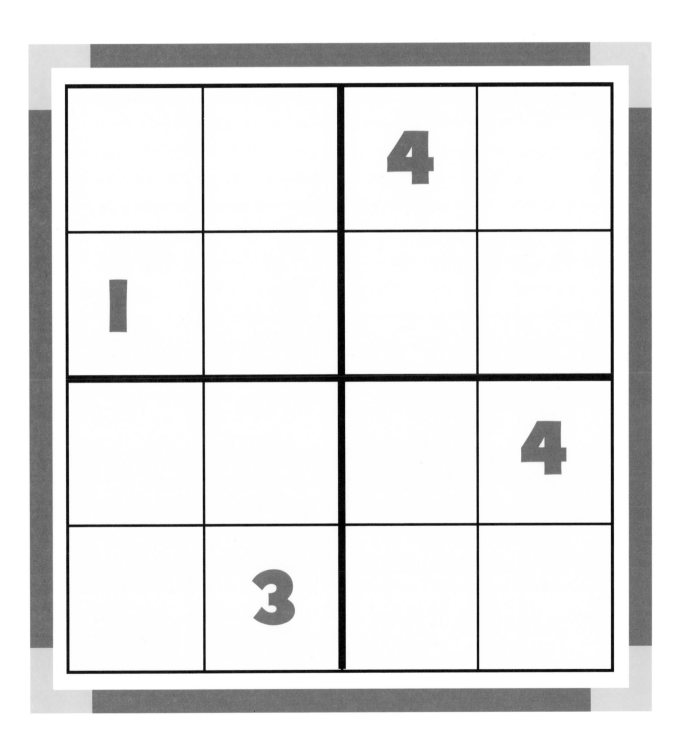

Small Pet

Solve this rebus puzzle to find out the name of a small pet.

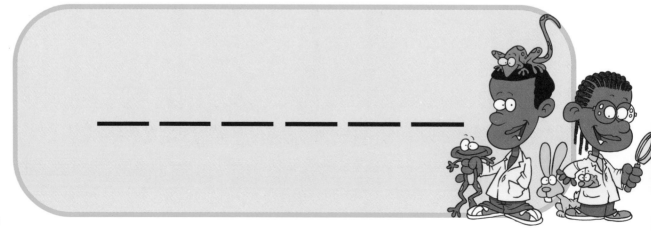

Answer on page 268

Scientific

Can you make **25** words or more from the following word?

SCIENTIFIC

151

Answer on page 268

A Pirate's Life

Find **10** differences between the picture on the left and the one on the right.

153

Funny Farm

Search, find, and circle these **10** things.

ACORN
BEACH BALL
BEES (3)

DEER
FLIES (3)
LIZARDS (2)
NECKTIE

RAKE
SNAIL
SUNGLASSES

Answer on page 269

Library Number

Guide this man to the library. Just follow the path of numbers that add up to **25**.

Start →

1	1	1	1	3
2		2		1
2		1		2

1	3	1	1	1	2	1
1		1		2		2
1	1	1	1	1	1	2

3	1
1	1	5

Finish →

Answer on page 269

Ocean Wildlife

Find these types of ocean wildlife in the word search.
Look up, down, backward, forward, and diagonally.

Fish   **Otter**
Shark   **Sea Turtle**
Dolphin   **Starfish**
Whale   **Oysters**
Seal   **Clams**

V	T	E	F	H	G	M	K	Y	G	C	O	U
N	A	O	E	I	O	N	R	D	G	S	Y	H
G	I	S	K	D	S	G	A	R	T	Q	S	S
V	R	H	R	C	K	X	H	J	D	P	T	I
L	V	S	P	Z	T	H	S	G	F	V	E	F
Q	A	V	S	L	P	X	O	T	T	E	R	R
B	P	E	U	P	O	K	L	Z	E	C	S	A
W	U	V	S	K	X	D	S	L	L	H	B	T
D	I	V	H	M	L	K	A	A	P	W	Z	S
F	W	Q	O	K	U	H	M	L	M	I	H	Y
A	I	W	F	A	W	S	U	K	P	D	G	O
E	D	S	E	L	T	R	U	T	A	E	S	Y
B	I	P	H	Q	S	C	Z	L	T	C	V	A

156

Multiplication

Use the clues below to complete this crossword puzzle.

aCROSS
1 6 x 3 =
2 9 x 1 =

DOWN
1 40 x 2 =
3 4 x 5 =

157

Read All About It

Use the clues below to complete this crossword puzzle.

ACROSS
3 Pictures and words
6 Out every day
7 Write it for school
9 Rhymes sometimes
10 Performed on a stage

DOWN
1 Weekly or monthly
2 Between two covers
4 Read it on screen
5 Small tale
8 Full-length fiction book

158

Decode-a-Riddle

Use the code key below to decode and solve this riddle.

A=Z	I=R	Q=J	Y=B	*=7
B=Y	J=Q	R=I	Z=A	#=8
C=X	K=P	S=H	!=I	>=9
D=W	L=O	T=G	@=2	+=0
E=V	M=N	U=F	<=3	
F=U	N=M	V=E	$=4	
G=T	O=L	W=D	%=5	
H=S	P=K	X=C	&=6	

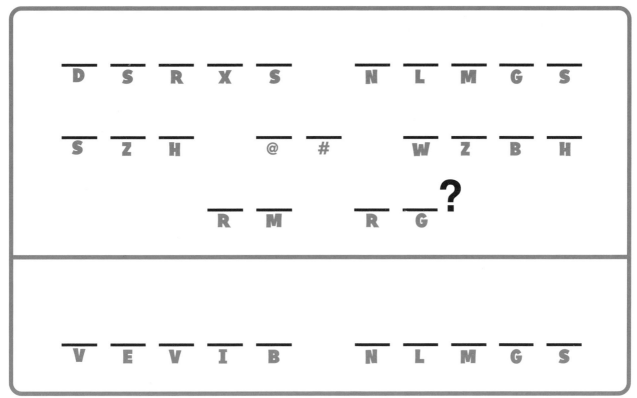

D S R X S   N L M G S

S Z H   @ #   W Z B H

R M   R G ?

V E V I B   N L M G S

Double Gumballs

Can you find the two pictures that are exactly alike?

Answer on page 271

Rattlesnake

Can you make **25** words or more from the following word?

RATTLESNAKE

Answer on page 271

Alien Odd Maze

Guide this alien to the spaceship by choosing the path made of **ODD** numbers only. You can only go **UP**, **DOWN**, and **ACROSS**—not diagonally.

Start

6	21	5	
7	3	8	2
15	10	16	8
1	7	13	1
16	8	9	6
4	6	5	2
11	11	3	1
3	4	5	2

Finish

Answer on page 271

Post Office

Use the pictures below to complete this crossword puzzle.

Answer on page 271

Type of Book

Solve this rebus puzzle to discover a type of helpful book.

– E +

– AR – ST +

– B – E +

– F – I

___ ___ ___ ___ ___ ___ ___ ___ ___ ___ ___

Answer on page 272

Farm Animals

Find these farm animals in the word search.
Look up, down, backward, forward, and diagonally.

PIG   COW

HORSE   GOAT

SHEEP   DUCK

ROOSTER   GEESE

CHICKEN   DOG

M	F	Z	E	K	Z	U	J	G	M	W	O	B
E	J	M	C	Y	C	H	I	C	K	E	N	Z
O	Q	U	C	N	X	N	R	Q	I	A	V	T
Z	D	S	Y	C	J	U	O	L	F	K	V	K
K	A	Y	S	V	Y	P	O	X	T	K	D	E
G	B	R	T	B	H	U	S	W	R	H	Q	D
J	D	D	B	J	J	W	T	Q	E	Y	R	S
S	Y	O	V	K	O	X	E	G	Z	W	Z	H
H	T	U	G	C	W	N	R	J	F	C	E	O
E	J	G	H	Y	R	S	C	P	R	P	S	R
E	G	O	O	E	O	Y	Q	U	I	L	E	S
P	O	A	C	U	X	Q	V	G	W	L	E	E
K	R	T	U	E	F	E	A	J	W	N	G	Z

165

Answer on page 272

Sudoku

Fill in the empty squares so that each row, column, and square box contains the numbers 1-9 only once.

		9		8		6		
	1				6	2		
8					5	7	4	1
		2				8		
1					2		3	
					4			2
	9			6				5
7		5	2				8	
	6		1			4	2	

Answer on page 272

Double Builders

Can you find the two pictures that are exactly alike?

167

Answer on page 272

Hockey Rink

Search, find, and circle these **10** things.

BASEBALLS (5)   **DOUGHNUT**   **LAMPSHADE**
CACTUS   **EARMUFFS**   **SNOWMAN**
CLARINET   **IGLOO**   **VIDEO CAMERA**
JACK-O'-LANTERN

Answer on page 273

Word Scramble

Unscramble each of these words using the clues.

WRAD
(Create a picture)

_ _ _ _

ETEHT
(They are in your mouth)

_ _ _ _ _

KAFE
(Not real)

_ _ _ _

PALEP
(Round, red fruit)

_ _ _ _ _

ESMRG
(They cause sickness)

_ _ _ _ _

NISGW
(Go back and forth)

_ _ _ _ _

LMKI
(Drink it with cookies)

_ _ _ _

DOCL
(Chilly, freezing)

_ _ _ _

Jungle Animals

Find these jungle animals in this word search. Look up, down, backward, forward, and diagonally.

LION	CROCODILE
ZEBRA	LIZARD
ELEPHANT	WOLF
BABOON	JAGUAR
CHEETAH	COUGAR

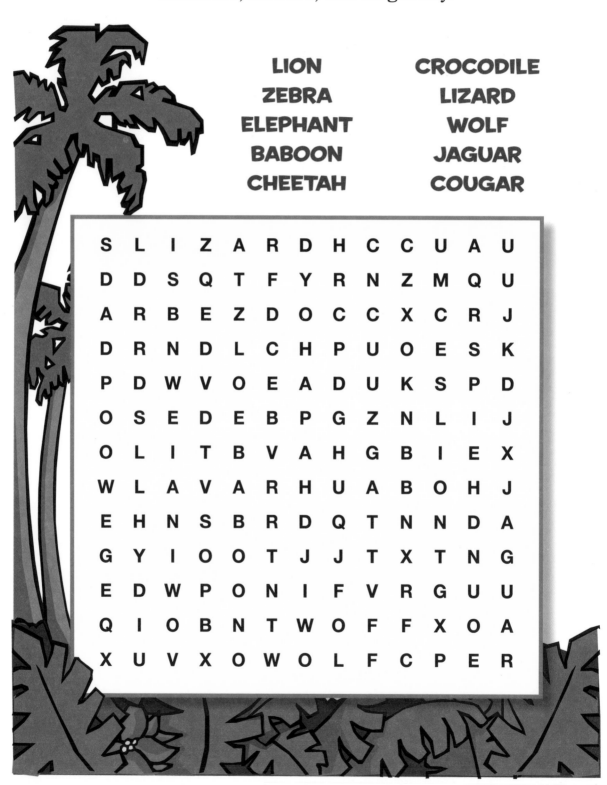

```
S  L  I  Z  A  R  D  H  C  C  U  A  U
D  D  S  Q  T  F  Y  R  N  Z  M  Q  U
A  R  B  E  Z  D  O  C  C  X  C  R  J
D  R  N  D  L  C  H  P  U  O  E  S  K
P  D  W  V  O  E  A  D  U  K  S  P  D
O  S  E  D  E  B  P  G  Z  N  L  I  J
O  L  I  T  B  V  A  H  G  B  I  E  X
W  L  A  V  A  R  H  U  A  B  O  H  J
E  H  N  S  B  R  D  Q  T  N  N  D  A
G  Y  I  O  O  T  J  J  T  X  T  N  G
E  D  W  P  O  N  I  F  V  R  G  U  U
Q  I  O  B  N  T  W  O  F  F  X  O  A
X  U  V  X  O  W  O  L  F  C  P  E  R
```

Answer on page 273

Sudoku

Fill in the empty squares so that each row, column, and square box contains the numbers **1 - 9** only once.

8	3	1	7			2		
7			2	5				4
		5				6		
3		9			5	7		
	8		3		1	4		2
1	5			7			8	9
5		4		8		9	2	
								6
2	6	8	9	4	3		1	7

Answer on page 273

Autumn

Use the clues below to complete this crossword puzzle.

across
1 The air gets ____
4 There is less and less _____
5 The trees get ____
6 Brightly colored leaves
7 Orange vegetables that can be carved
8 Put away light jackets, put on _____
10 Gathering of crops
11 The season to prepare for _____

DOWN
2 What falls in autumn
3 Light up the ____
6 Another name for autumn
9 Can harm delicate plants

Answer on page 274

Decode-a-Message

What's today's lead story? Use the code key below to find out what happened.

1=A	8=H	15=O	22=V
2=B	9=I	16=P	23=W
3=C	10=J	17=Q	24=X
4=D	11=K	18=R	25=Y
5=E	12=L	19=S	26=Z
6=F	13=M	20=T	
7=G	14=N	21=U	

```
___ ___ ___   ___ ___   ___ ___ ___ ___
 3   1   20    9   14    20  18   5   5

___ ___   ___ ___ ___ ___ ___   ___ ___
 9   19    19   1  22   5   4     2   25

      ___ ___ ___ ___ ___ ___ ___!
       6   9   18   5  13   1   14
```

173

Double Jack-o'-lanterns

Can you find the two pictures that are exactly alike?

Answer on page 274

Scatterbrain

Can you make **25** words or more from the following word?

SCATTERBRAIN

Even Maze

Begin at **Start** and make your way to **Finish** by jumping from one **even** number to the next. Move only on even, not odd, numbers. You can only go **UP**, **DOWN**, and **ACROSS**—not diagonally.

Start

2	4	6	7	9	1	3	5
7	9	8	3	5	7	9	1
3	5	6	4	2	3	5	7
9	1	3	5	8	2	4	3
5	7	9	1	3	5	8	9
1	3	5	7	9	1	6	8
7	9	1	3	5	7	9	2
3	5	7	9	1	3	5	4

Finish

176

Types of Vegetables

Find these types of vegetables in this word search.
Look up, down, backward, forward, and diagonally.

Carrot   Pepper   Radish   Broccoli   Asparagus
Cucumber   Lettuce   Celery   Artichoke   Squash

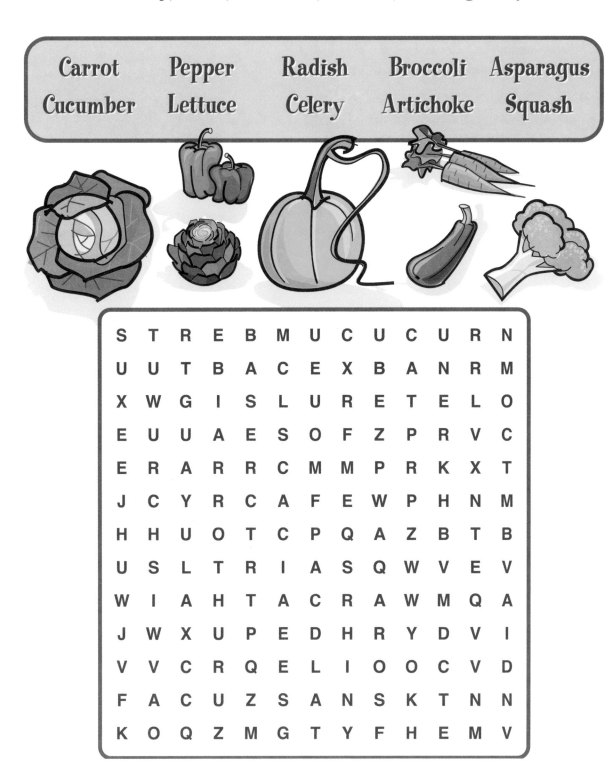

```
S T R E B M U C U C U R N
U U T B A C E X B A N R M
X W G I S L U R E T E L O
E U U A E S O F Z P R V C
E R A R R C M M P R K X T
J C Y R C A F E W P H N M
H H U O T C P Q A Z B T B
U S L T R I A S Q W V E V
W I A H T A C R A W M Q A
J W X U P E D H R Y D V I
V V C R Q E L I O O C V D
F A C U Z S A N S K T N N
K O Q Z M G T Y F H E M V
```

177

Family

Solve this rebus puzzle to find a popular expression about the family.

+ **IS** +

− **AL** + **RE** + −

− **IMBL** + +

− **F** − **H**

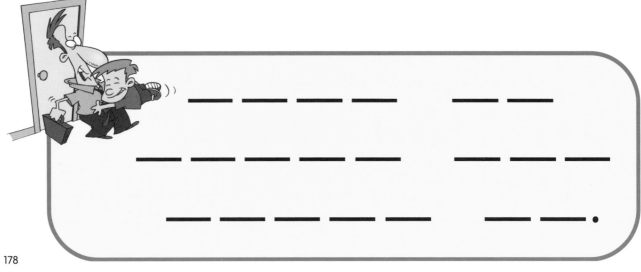

_ _ _ _ _ _ _ _ _

_ _ _ _ _ _ _ _ _ _ _

_ _ _ _ _ _ _ _ .

178

Sudoku

Fill in the empty squares so that each row, column, and square box contains the numbers **1** - **9** only once.

7		3			9			
			7	3	8	5	6	
				6		2		7
		7		4	3			2
	2			7			4	
8				9		7		
1		5		2				
	3	6	4	1	7			
			3			6		1

179

Answer on page 275

Can You Canoe?

Find **10** differences between the picture on the left and the one on the right.

181

Sky High Fun

Search, find, and circle these **10** things.

BOOK	HOT DOG	TV
CACTUS	ICE-CREAM CONE	SALT SHAKER
GORILLA	NECKTIE	STRAWBERRY
	PIE	

182

Word Scramble

Unscramble each of these words using the clues.

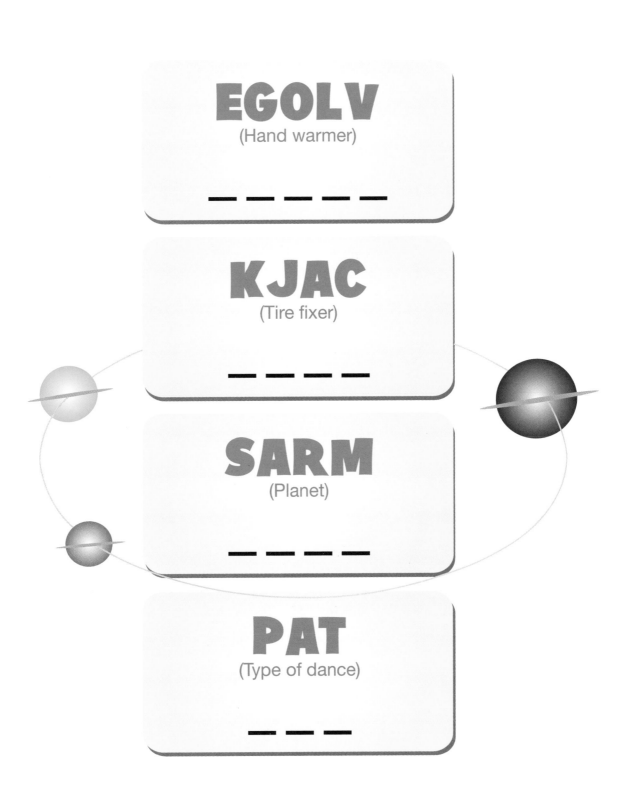

EGOLV
(Hand warmer)

_ _ _ _ _

KJAC
(Tire fixer)

_ _ _ _

SARM
(Planet)

_ _ _ _

PAT
(Type of dance)

_ _ _

Answer on page 276

Types of Dogs

Find these types of dogs in the word search.
Look up, down, backward, forward, and diagonally.

Afghan
Beagle
Chihuahua
Dalmatian
Greyhound

Havanese
Labrador
Maltese

Poodle
Weimaraner

K Q U G B B J V S D P J R X F
B T J F R F L W S K Q C U C F
X E U C O E F E S Q H C A A W
X Y A T H Y Y M S A F U L N R
R H M G I I R H V E O D A R E
D H T B L Y H A O R T H B J N
G Y L S A E N U D U G L R P A
W V P B J E K A A F N D A D R
E C P S S C L N A H T D D M A
M R Z E I M C K H I U B O K M
V X G T A O H F F Y X A R N I
U E Q T Y Y Z V L K L Y C F E
P Y I H T E L D O O P L B Q W
Y A L H M R L N H D W N Y T N
N S E I G R I Z D L B N K M R

Answer on page 277

Add It Up

Use the clues below to complete this crossword puzzle.

ACROSS
1 9 + 8 =
2 18 + 11 =

DOWN
1 24 + 36 =
3 16 + 24 =

Answer on page 277

Jigsaw Puzzle

Can you make **25** words or more from the following phrase?

JIGSAW PUZZLE

_____

_____ _____

_____ _____

_____ _____

_____ _____

_____ _____

_____ _____

_____ _____

_____ _____

_____ _____

_____ _____

_____ _____

Answer on page 277

Math Code

Solve each equation, then use the code key to learn what is the most popular pet in the U.S.

7 - 5 + 1 = ☐

3 + 4 - 6 = ☐

10 x 2 = ☐

5 + 6 + 8 = ☐

1=A	2=B	3=C	4=D	5=E
6=F	7=G	8=H	9=I	10=J
11=K	12=L	13=M	14=N	15=O
16=P	17=Q	18=R	19=S	20=T
21=U	22=V	23=W	24=X	25=Y
26=Z				

____ ____ ____ ____

Double Princesses

Can you find the two pictures that are exactly alike?

Answer on page 278

Scary Stuff

Use the clues below to complete this crossword puzzle.

ACROSS
4 Flying mammal
5 All bones
6 Spirit that lives on
7 Another word for spooky

DOWN
1 Living dead that feeds on blood
2 Spell caster
3 Inhuman creature

Answer on page 278

Superhero Maze

Guide this superhero to Earth by choosing the path made of **EVEN** numbers only. You can only go **UP**, **DOWN**, and **ACROSS**—not diagonally.

Start

6	14	8	2	10	16	4	
3	6	13	21	5	12	11	
9	12	19	6	15	23	3	5
8	4	6	2	20	6	22	4
11	17	13	3	9	7	11	8
1	18	14	6	5	16	10	2
21	8	17	20	7	6	3	12
17	4	1	2	8	12	1	2
13	6	14	13	12	9	13	12
17	4	19	20	21	22	20	21
5	2	12	35	26	25	35	26
7	15	16	13	12	9	13	12
8	18	10	20	21	22	20	21
9	19	17	13	15	22	20	17

Finish

Amusement Park

Use the pictures below to complete this crossword puzzle.

1. Guess your _____   2. Roller _____   3. _____-go-round   4. Fortune _____

Answer on page 278

Ocean Life

Solve this rebus puzzle to find something that lives in the ocean.

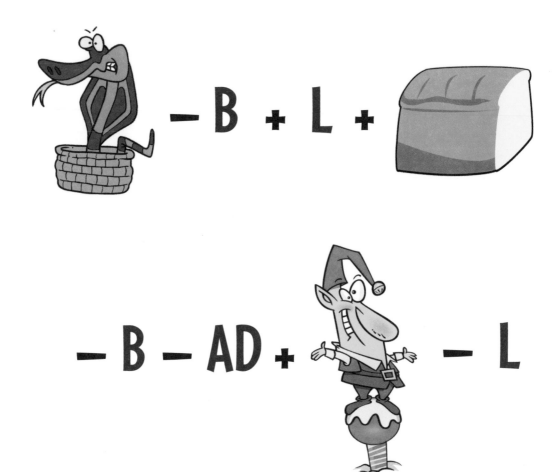

_ _ _ _ _

_ _ _ _ _

Answer on page 279

Ice-Cream Stand

Find **two sets of two objects** that rhyme with each other.

Answer on page 279

Types Of Cookies

Find these types of cookies in the word search. Look up, down, backward, forward, and diagonally.

Oatmeal   Snickerdoodle
Chocolate chip   Butter
Peanut butter   Gingersnap
Sugar   Linzer
Shortbread   Biscotti

Q L G E O G G Z L M A O N P R
W I T T O C S I B I O S E M X
P S S E S Q Y S D E N A B C S
I S Y F U Q O M X M N Z E K N
H N H X G L H K H U X T E B I
C P Z O A F T L T T P E T R C
E A D J R B Y B A E A R W A K
T N L W G T U P L E F G Q I E
A S R N I T B H K Z M T G F R
L R Z E T O U R C S H T P Q D
O E Y E T F L B E S X S A D O
C G R C O T E W K A Y E D O O
O N S V D J U B H S D H R B D
H I N Q B F U B V R O S C M L
C G Q A H I G U N S Z E K A E

194

Ready For Take-Off

Use the clues below to complete this crossword puzzle.

ACROSS
1 Rest your head.
3 Lean against
7 Really fast plane
8 Put your food on
10 Where the pilot sits
11 Serves the food

DOWN
1 Get on board the ___ .
2 Provides the power
4 What the pilots operate
5 Keeps you strapped in
6 It floats.
9 Flies the plane

Answer on page 279

Jungle Jamboree

Search, find, and circle these **10** things.

ALIEN
BASEBALL CAP
BUTTERFLIES (2)

GOLF CLUB
MICE (2)
PANDA
TOP HATS (3)

HANDKERCHIEF
HARMONICA
TRUMPET

Answer on page 280

Word Scramble

Unscramble each of these words using the clues.

HTILG
(Brightens room)

_ _ _ _ _

PYPHA
(Emotion)

_ _ _ _ _

LDOWR
(Where we live)

_ _ _ _ _

NKIG
(Ruler)

_ _ _ _

All-Star Hockey

Find the things that have to do with hockey in the word search.
Look up, down, backward, forward, and diagonally.

Puck
Pad
Assist
Goalie
Pass

Penalty
Interference
Overtime
Rebound
Breakaway

B	L	O	B	I	B	N	C	M	W	M	D	S	O
V	P	J	E	I	X	U	C	M	K	C	U	P	P
E	C	N	E	R	E	F	R	E	T	N	I	L	L
J	P	A	S	S	Z	W	B	U	F	E	K	G	J
F	H	K	G	Z	T	P	M	Q	Z	P	T	R	V
E	Q	A	K	Y	A	W	A	K	A	E	R	B	E
K	M	A	W	D	W	B	T	D	F	B	Q	F	Q
L	Z	I	A	R	E	B	O	U	N	D	A	L	T
V	B	G	T	S	N	Y	T	L	A	N	E	P	A
V	R	T	O	R	S	D	C	K	A	E	W	W	Y
X	R	H	Q	A	E	I	V	S	I	C	L	J	D
H	I	Z	P	F	L	V	S	X	Q	D	D	V	Q
L	A	R	M	F	N	I	O	T	D	D	J	S	Z
W	B	M	F	E	L	S	E	U	P	N	F	M	H

Answer on page 280

Sudoku

Fill in the empty squares so that each row, column, and square box contains the numbers **1-9** only once.

1		6		3				4
		3	6		4	8		5
4	2		9		5	6		3
8	9				3	4		
	1		4	9	6	5		
	6	4	5				3	9
5			1		9		4	
6	3	9		4	2	1		8
				5		2		6

199

Flying Machines

Use the clues below to complete this crossword puzzle.

across
1. Presidential
2. Outer space
3. Wright brothers
4. Commercial airliner
5. Lands on water

DOWN
6. Hot air
7. Rotors
8. Silent military

Answer on page 281

Decode-a-Message

Solve each equation, then use the code key to learn the name of the closest planet to Earth.

(40 ÷ 2) + 2 = ☐

(4 x 5) - 15 = ☐

(100 ÷ 10) + 4 = ☐

3 + 4 + 7 + 2 + 5 = ☐

(7 x 3) - 2 = ☐

1=A	2=B	3=C	4=D	5=E	6=F
7=G	8=H	9=I	10=J	11=K	12=L
13=M	14=N	15=O	16=P	17=Q	18=R
19=S	20=T	21=U	22=V	23=W	24=X
25=Y	26=Z				

___ ___ ___ ___ ___

Answer on page 281

Cooking Utensils

Find these cooking utensils in this word search.
Look up, down, backward, forward, and diagonally.

Knife   Thermometer
Whisk   Masher
Spatula   Shredder
Scraper   Grater
Measuring cup   Blender

```
J  E  C  P  J  Z  D  P  J  X  K  Z  U  Z  R
B  L  E  N  D  E  R  I  Z  D  Q  N  K  X  E
O  N  S  Y  N  E  M  R  P  B  B  B  O  L  T
A  Y  T  S  T  F  E  A  U  I  L  N  H  Q  E
O  C  N  A  B  H  N  F  C  E  J  P  S  S  M
N  L  R  Z  S  D  W  E  G  G  V  L  H  F  O
Q  G  S  A  M  D  E  H  N  W  P  L  R  Q  M
T  A  M  U  R  U  K  K  I  V  I  O  E  D  R
Y  W  G  Q  D  M  A  E  R  C  N  N  D  J  E
S  Q  C  Q  Y  D  S  I  U  S  L  U  D  S  H
K  B  K  Q  R  C  X  K  S  I  H  W  E  E  T
W  F  E  F  I  N  K  S  A  E  P  F  R  H  E
A  T  G  Q  X  V  B  Q  E  T  L  J  B  X  G
H  S  P  A  T  U  L  A  M  N  A  D  P  O  Q
E  Z  R  E  P  A  R  C  S  E  W  N  U  N  D
```

202

Haunted House

Can you make **25** words or more from the following phrase?

HAUNTED HOUSE

Answer on page 281

Lucky Number One

Going from **Start** to **Finish**, choose the path
made up of the number **1** only.

Start

1	1	8	4	2
5	1	3	3	6
4	1	1	8	8
2	5	1	1	9
7	4	6	1	7
9	8	3	1	1

Finish

Answer on page 282

Time to Bake!

Unscramble the clues below to complete this crossword puzzle.

ACROSS

1 LNAVILA _____

2 GEG _____

3 LORUF _____

4 TRETBU _____

DOWN

5 KGBANI WOPEDR

_____ _____

6 GUSRA _____

Answer on page 282

Vehicle

Solve this rebus puzzle to find something that can get you somewhere in a hurry.

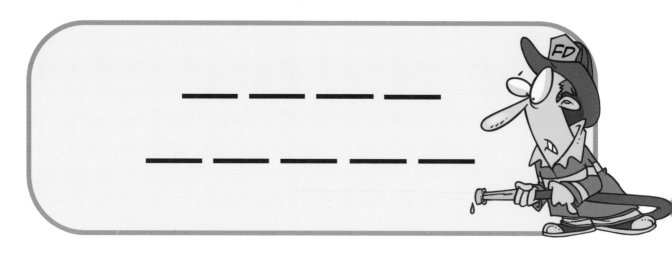

Answer on page 282

Decode-a-Riddle

Use the code key below to decode and solve this riddle.

1=A	8=H	15=O	22=V
2=B	9=I	16=P	23=W
3=C	10=J	17=Q	24=X
4=D	11=K	18=R	25=Y
5=E	12=L	19=S	26=Z
6=F	13=M	20=T	21=U
7=G	14=N	21=U	

```
___  ___  ___  ___     ___  ___     ___  ___  ___
23   8    1    20      4    15      25   15   21

___  ___  ___  ___     ___       ___  ___  ___  ___  ___  ___
3    1    12   12      1         26   9    16   16   5    18

___  ___       ___       ___  ___  ___  ___  ___  ___ ?
15   14        1         2    1    14   1    14   1

___       ___  ___  ___  ___  ___      ___  ___  ___
1         6    18   21   9    20       6    12   25
```

207

One, Two, Three, Fore?

Find **10** differences between the picture on the left and the one on the right.

209

Answer on page 283

Pirates Ahoy!

Search, find, and circle these **10** things.

BASKETBALL
BIRDS' NEST
CLOWNS (2)

FLOWERPOTS (4)
GINGERBREAD MAN
JACK-O'-LANTERN
MONKEY

MUMMY
PARKING METER
PENCIL

Answer on page 283

Water Maze

Follow the path from **Start** to **Finish** to get
the water mobiles to the finish line.

211

Animals in Hibernation

Find these types of hibernating animals in this word search.
Look up, down, backward, forward, and diagonally.

BEAR
FROG
BAT

SQUIRREL
HEDGEHOG
RACCOON
SKUNK

CHIPMUNK
BADGER
HAMSTER

```
G R L R F N W Y Q Y G R V
L J M S A F C R T U Y T P
M E Q F G E Q A J U B N Z
W K R Y M O B H Z A S O X
D O C R E D E M D H B O U
G E C N I D Y G J A N C A
T X C H G U E O T M O C S
B B Z E I R Q K T S V A K
Z N H L M P X S D T E R U
K O A D F B M F U E M O N
G O M A C F E U C R B O K
C D O D R V K R N X E N U
N T R F H C D Q W K R X V
```

Answer on page 284

Get to Work

Unscramble these computer terms in the blanks below and then place them in the crossword puzzle.

ACROSS
1 ARDH RDVIE
_____

2 UOSME
_____

3 MPERTUOC
_____

DOWN
2 NOIMROT
_____

4 UORRET
_____

5 ROABDYEK
_____

213

Down Under

Use the clues below to complete this crossword puzzle.

ACROSS
3 Rock-like animals
7 Hard shells
9 They swim in schools.
10 Humans staying underwater

DOWN
1 Swimmers, beware!
2 Shocking!
4 Undersea vessel
5 Half-human creature of legend
6 Many legs
8 Green plant life

Answer on page 284

Word Game

Look at the pictures below. Figure out what phrase uses these words and fill it in on the lines below.

— — — — —

— — —   — — — —

— — — — — — —

215

Road Signs

Find these road signs in this word search.
Look up, down, backward, forward, and diagonally.

Speed Limit	Caution
Stop	Do Not Enter
Dead End	Yield
One Way	No Parking
Slow	Parking

```
R  D  E  A  D  E  N  D  L  F  N  T  P  T
M  U  J  O  Z  Z  O  B  C  A  T  A  O  N
V  T  W  F  D  F  T  Y  P  I  R  D  B  O
E  Y  P  E  O  P  J  H  M  K  L  F  W  I
A  I  N  I  N  C  L  I  I  Z  E  G  O  T
A  E  O  K  O  D  L  N  J  T  S  N  G  U
G  L  N  I  T  D  G  U  P  Y  E  I  R  A
L  D  P  W  E  F  X  C  J  W  E  K  A  C
I  F  U  E  N  B  P  N  A  E  F  R  U  V
V  F  P  S  T  O  P  Y  V  A  L  A  P  O
H  S  V  G  E  A  V  E  Y  K  O  P  S  N
Q  V  Y  X  R  Y  H  S  L  O  W  O  V  F
F  D  V  F  G  U  T  X  O  I  V  N  J  L
D  D  C  P  S  J  C  E  T  B  R  W  O  A
```

216

Rollercoaster

Can you make **25** words or more from the following word?

ROLLERCOASTER

Star Number Maze

Guide this astronomer through this maze to the stars by putting
1 to **25** in the correct order.

Answer on page 285

Decode-a-Riddle

Use the code key below to decode and solve this riddle.

A=!	G=&	M=:	S="	X=\
B=@	H=*	N=<	T='	Y=}
C=#	I=(	O=>	U='	Z={
D=$	J=+	P=[	V=?	
E=%	K=)	Q=]	W=/	
F=^	L=;	R="		

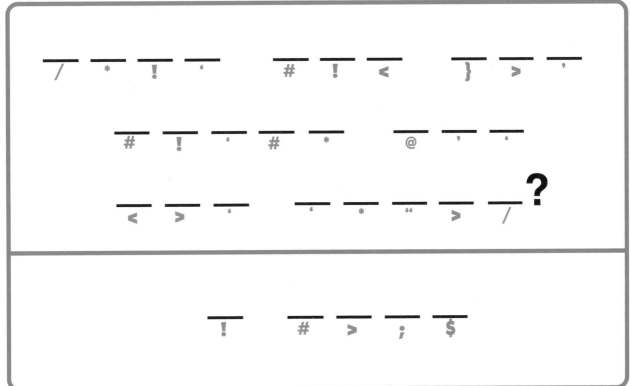

WHAT CAN YOU

CATCH BUT

NOT THROW?

A COLD

Office Supplies

Solve this rebus puzzle to find something you use in an office.

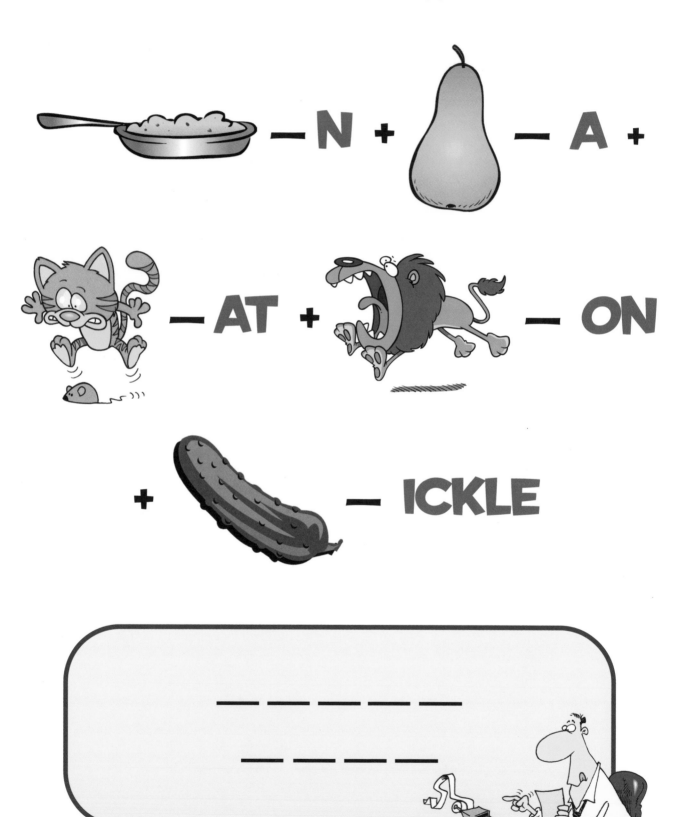

Answer on page 286

Double Cellos

Can you find the two pictures that are exactly alike?

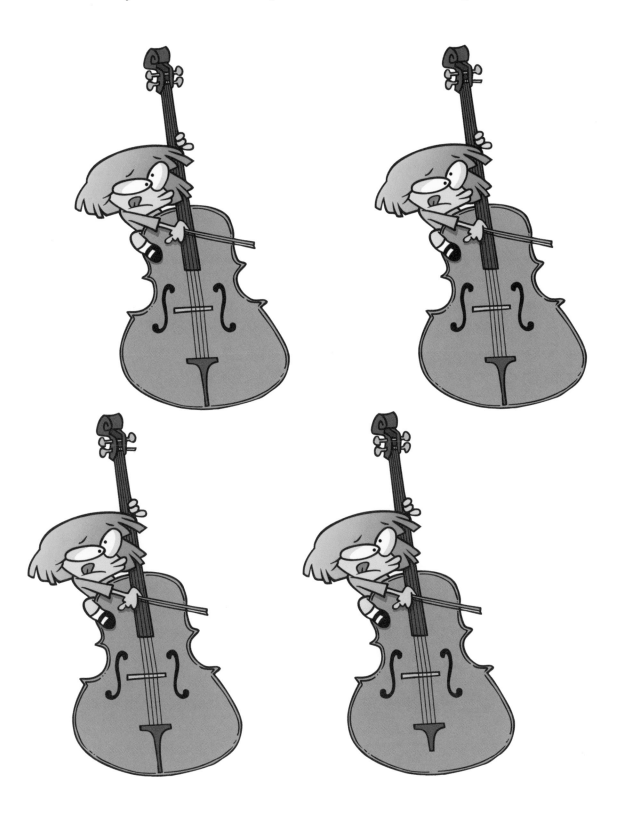

Answer on page 286

Chess

Find these things in the word search that have to do with chess.
Look up, down, backward, forward, and diagonally.

Pawn   **Knight**
Bishop   **Queen**
Tournament   **Forfeit**
Checkmate   **Score**
King   **Rank**

```
Y S I Y X B O T F R G W B P
I I C U F Z N G X B Y Q A Q
O L Q O X V N O C V U W P K
I D W L R I S N Z E V O T D
X L W W K E S U E J H O G S
K E T M W G L N P S U P U T
M T D R T X P J I R A A H K
N A K F L H F B N B Y W E K
G M Y J O X G A T O W N H P
X K Q P E R M I R R Y J U S
H C C W C E F C N A W X L I
I E X V N N K E A K N F W F
P H H T S G I N I P H K X G
E C S H K T P P A T R L M U
```

State Birds

Put the state bird of each state in the crossword below.

ACROSS
3 Michigan
6 Iowa
8 California
11 New Mexico
12 Vermont

DOWN
1 Maryland
2 Tennessee
4 Colorado
5 New York
7 Indiana
9 Georgia
10 Arizona

223

Answer on page 286

Dancing Diner

Search, find, and circle these **10** things.

APPLES (2)   DRUM   RHINOCEROS
BIRDS (2)   FRANKENSTEIN   PUMPKIN
CROWN   NECKTIES (2)   WATERMELON
      PENGUIN

224

Answer on page 287

Sudoku

Fill in the empty squares so that each row, column, and square box contains the numbers **1-4** only once.

Answer on page 287

Types of Cakes

Find these types of cakes in the word search.
Look up, down, backward, forward, and diagonally.

Pound
Chocolate
Shortcake
Coffee
Cheesecake

Ice cream
Carrot
Red Velvet
Birthday
Wedding

```
O M X O P R H W A O A A J D R
Q A T M S D B I R T H D A Y E
Z E N W Y W V J D D X P U J H
E R E C H E E S E C A K E D R
Z C T K C V G Y L X M O N R G
K E C G A X M C R F B U T R M
M C H T K C U L Y S O E L E P
H I O I V U T H G P J U U D I
M C C E T N O R G D G Q H V I
A T O P E Z E R O N L S E E K
J O L C L F D K I H C Y U L H
X R A Q D Y F D L N S I Q V V
U R T C O P D O Z U C B Q E P
S A E T K E P X C Q C Q G T Z
W C S E W J L B N G N C D J V
```

226

USA Maze

Follow the path from **Start** to **Finish** to get from the east coast to the west coast.

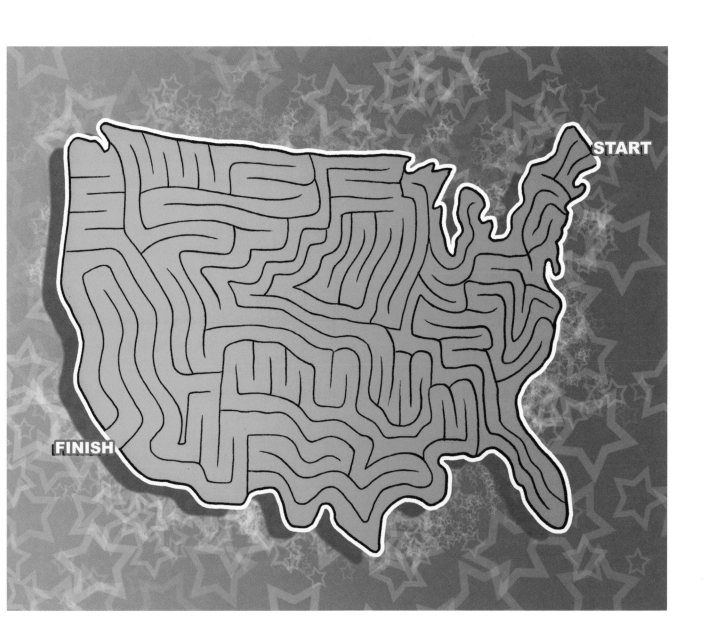

227

Double Geese

Can you find the two pictures that are exactly alike?

Answer on page 288

Decode-a-Riddle

Use the code key below to decode and solve this riddle.

A=!	E=%	I=(	M=:	Q=]	U='	Y=}
B=@	F=^	J=+	N=<	R="	V=?	Z={
C=#	G=&	K=)	O=>	S="	W=/	
D=$	H=*	L=;	P=[	T='	X=\	

/ * % " % $ > % "

^ " ($! }   # > : %

@ % ^ > " %   ' * ' " " $! } ?

(<   ' * %

$ (# ' (> < ! " }

229

Answer on page 288

Technology

Solve this rebus puzzle to find something that involves a mouse.

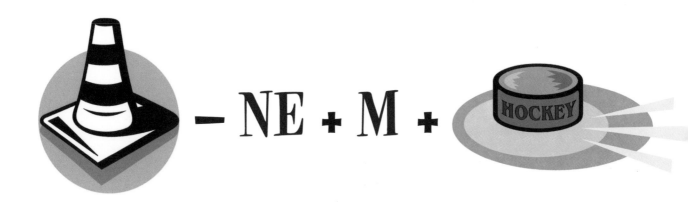

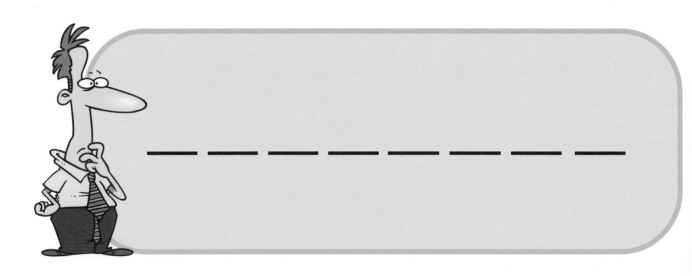

Answer on page 288

Out In Space

Use the clues below to complete this crossword puzzle.

ACROSS
3 Our closest neighbor in space
4 The red planet
7 Chunk of a planet
8 The ringed planet

DOWN
1 Twinkling in the night sky
2 Source of light and heat
3 Our galaxy
4 The hottest planet
5 Streaks through space with a tail
6 The biggest planet

231

Answers

Page 4
Rhyme Time

1) SEA (body part) _____
2) HOWL (garden tool) _____
3) FIRST (explode) _____
4) HARP (pointy) _____
5) HEIGHT (chew) _____
6) FROWN (funny guy) _____
7) SPONGE (fall) _____

1. K N E E
2. T R O W E L
3. B U R S T
4. S H A R P
5. B I T E
6. C L O W N
7. P L U N G E

Page 5
In Action

ACROSS
1. On skates, bikes, or scooters
4. Go high in the air
5. Up a tree or mountain
7. To stroll

DOWN
2. Big jump
3. Don't leave the water _____
5. Babies, before walking
6. Birds and planes and kites

1. R O L L
2. L E A P
3. R
4. J U M P
  R U N N I N G
5. C L I M B I N G
  C R A W L I N G
6. F
7. W A L K
  F L Y

Page 6
Decode-a-Riddle

W H A T   M A D E
Z K D W   P D G H

T H E   O C T O P U S
W K H   R F W R S X V

G I G G L E ?
J L J J O H

E I G H T   T I C K L E S
H L J K W   W L F N O H V

Page 7
Double Popsicles

232

Answers

Page 8
Fascination

FASCINATION

Here are just a few:

act	coin	fits	sift
acts	cost	icon	sit
ant	cot	inn	sofa
ants	fact	into	soft
can	fan	not	son
cans	fast	oat	taco
cast	fat	oats	tan
cat	fin	sat	tin
cats	fist	scan	ton
coat	fit	scat	tons

Page 9
Rockin' Ray Maze

Page 10
Trucks

Page 11
Poetic Puzzle

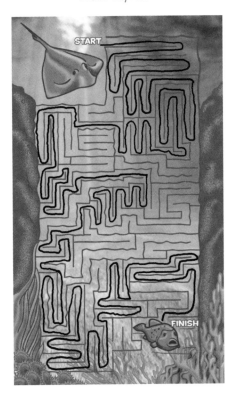

E + [glass] − K + Y

D + [ice] − E + [king]

− G + S + **1** − E

<u>E</u> <u>M</u> <u>I</u> <u>L</u> <u>Y</u>
<u>D</u> <u>I</u> <u>C</u> <u>K</u> <u>I</u> <u>N</u> <u>S</u> <u>O</u> <u>N</u>

Answers

Page 12
Lazy Sunday

Page 13
State Capitals

Page 14
Bust-a-Beat

Page 15

Answers

Page 16
Word Scramble

RBID
(Likes to fly)

B I R D

NUJE
(Summer month)

J U N E

CEID
(Number game)

D I C E

TCHAW
(Tells time)

W A T C H

Page 17
Fishing

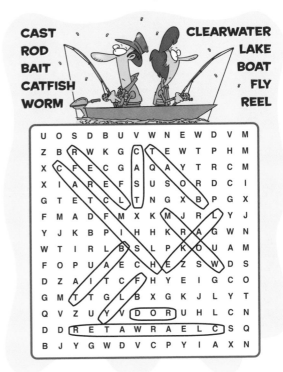

CAST
ROD
BAIT
CATFISH
WORM

CLEARWATER
LAKE
BOAT
FLY
REEL

```
U O S D B U V W N E W D V M
Z B R W K G C T E W T P H M
X C F E C G A Q A Y T R C M
X I A R E F S U S O R D C I
G E T C L T N G X B P G E X
F M A D F M X K M J R L Y J
Y J K B P H H R A G W N
W T I R L B S L P K O U A M
F O P U A E C H E Z S W D S
D Z A I T C F H Y E I G C O
G M T T G L B X G K J L Y
Q V Z U Y V D O R U H L C N
D D R E T A W R A E L C S Q
B J Y G W D V C P Y I A X N
```

Page 18
Where Am I?

across	Down
3 Circling	1 Not indoors
5 Hidden in back of	2 Enter the building
6 In the middle	4 Above
7 Beneath	6 Next to

Crossword solution:
- 1 (down) OUTSIDE
- 2 (down) INSIDE
- 3 (across) AROUND
- 4 (down) OVER
- 5 (across) BEHIND
- 6 (across) BETWEEN
- 6 (down) BESIDE
- 7 (across) UNDER

Page 19
Decode-a-Message

A=3	D=9	N=10	R=2
B=11	E=1	O=8	Y=4
C=6	L=5	P=7	

R E D   C R A Y O N
2 1 9   6 2 3 4 8 10

235

Answers

Page 20
Word Game

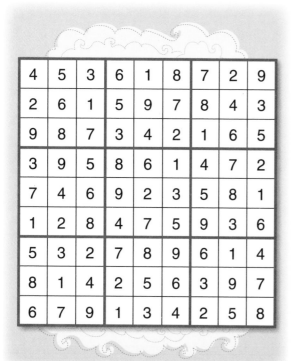

P O P G O E S
T H E W E A S E L.

Page 21
Celebration

CELEBRATION

Here are just a few:

able	boil	neat	riot
ace	canoe	oat	tea
acne	clone	ocean	teal
acorn	clot	rain	tear
actor	ice	ran	teen
air	icon	rate	ten
alert	into	ratio	tire
aloe	lace	real	tone
bake	learn	reel	tree
baton	nail	rib	
bear	near	rice	

Page 22
Sudoku

4	5	3	6	1	8	7	2	9
2	6	1	5	9	7	8	4	3
9	8	7	3	4	2	1	6	5
3	9	5	8	6	1	4	7	2
7	4	6	9	2	3	5	8	1
1	2	8	4	7	5	9	3	6
5	3	2	7	8	9	6	1	4
8	1	4	2	5	6	3	9	7
6	7	9	1	3	4	2	5	8

Page 23
Ballerina

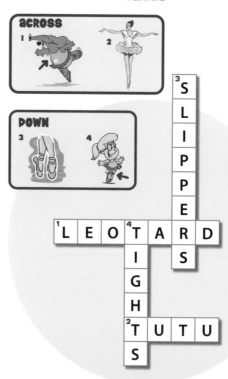

Answers

Page 24
Slippery Stuff

<u>B</u> <u>A</u> <u>N</u> <u>A</u> <u>N</u> <u>A</u>
<u>P</u> <u>E</u> <u>E</u> <u>L</u>

Page 25
Creative Puzzle

<u>B</u> <u>E</u> <u>E</u>'<u>S</u>
<u>K</u> <u>N</u> <u>E</u> <u>E</u> <u>S</u>.

Page 26
Take a Trip

across
1 You need these for the plane or train
5 Things to remember your trip by
6 Where to eat on a trip
8 Reference for info
9 Pack this up with clothes
10 Book in advance

DOWN
2 Snap those pictures
3 Mail these to your friends
4 Best seats on the plane
7 Leads you in a new place

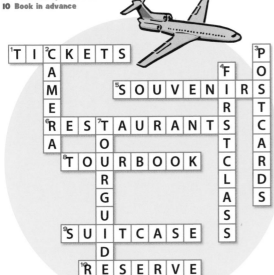

¹TICKETS
²C A M E R A
³P O S T C A R D S
⁴F I R S T C L A S S
⁵SOUVENIRS
⁶RESTAURANTS
⁷T O U R G U I D E
⁸TOURBOOK
⁹SUITCASE
¹⁰RESERVE

Page 27
Sudoku

3	9	1	5	8	4	2	7	6
2	5	7	1	3	6	8	4	9
8	6	4	2	9	7	3	5	1
6	8	3	7	2	1	5	9	4
5	7	9	4	6	3	1	2	8
1	4	2	8	5	9	6	3	7
7	3	8	9	1	5	4	6	2
4	2	6	3	7	8	9	1	5
9	1	5	6	4	2	7	8	3

237

Answers

Page 28
Strike Out

Page 29
Word Scramble

ILDAGFRUE
(Water rescue)
L I F E G U A R D

SGNATYM
(Athlete)
G Y M N A S T

AUMERSETPKR
(Food source)
S U P E R M A R K E T

AAGORKON
(Animal)
K A N G A R O O

IMEETTSLO
(Christmas leaves hung in doorway)
M I S T L E T O E

NUUAMT
(Season)
A U T U M N

EAMDMRI
(Fishy person)
M E R M A I D

ALANSAG
(Food)
L A S A G N A

Page 30
Tennis

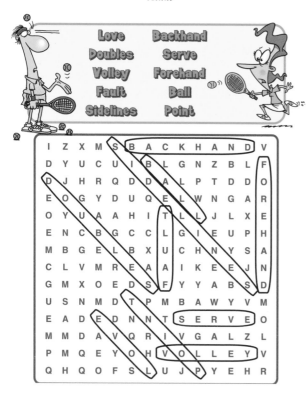

Love Backhand
Doubles Serve
Volley Forehand
Fault Ball
Sidelines Point

Page 31
Lucky Number Three

Start

3	2	4	4	2
3	1	8	7	6
3	3	1	5	8
2	3	1	6	9
7	3	6	8	7
9	3	3	3	3

Finish

Answers

Page 32
Rescue Vehicles

ACROSS	DOWN
1 Broken leg	4 Burglar
2 House fire	5 Sea distress
3 Search and rescue	

Page 33
Decode-a-Riddle

A=5	E=6	I=2	M=3	S=4
C=11	G=13	K=7	N=12	U=14
D=1	H=9	L=8	P=10	

C	H	I	C	K	E	N		A	N	D
11	9	2	11	7	6	12		5	12	1

D	U	M	P	L	I	N	G	S
1	14	3	10	8	2	12	13	4

Page 34
Double Octopuses

Page 35
A Balanced Diet

A BALANCED DIET

Here are just a few:

acid	dad	idea	nail
aid	dance	lace	need
bad	data	land	net
bald	dead	late	nice
band	dealt	lead	tab
bleed	debit	lean	table
can	deli	lend	tail
canal	dine	lent	tale
candle	eat	lice	tan
cane	elite	lid	tea
dab	ice	lie	tile

239

Answers

Page 36
Odd Birthday Maze

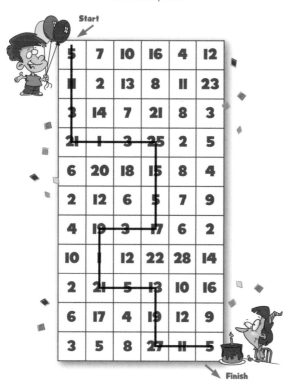

Page 37
Holiday Time

Page 38
Super Singer

<u>P</u> <u>O</u> <u>P</u>

<u>S</u> <u>T</u> <u>A</u> <u>R</u>

Page 39
Hardware Store

Answers

Page 40
Pumpkin Harvest

Page 41

Page 42
U.S. Cities

across
2 The White House
3 Hollywood
5 Mile high
7 Golden Gate Bridge
8 Paul Revere

DOWN
1 Liberty Bell
4 Sears Tower
6 Empire State Building

Crossword answers:
- 2 WASHINGTONDC
- 3 LOSANGELES
- 5 DENVER
- 7 SANFRANCISCO
- 8 BOSTON
- 1 PHILADELPHIA
- 4 CHICAGO
- 6 NEWYORK

Page 43
Word Scramble

REFLWO
(Blooming plant)
F L O W E R

LDSALA
(Texas city)
D A L L A S

GLUJEN
(Land of thick vegetation)
J U N G L E

HTEGI
(Not seven or nine)
E I G H T

LETBLA
(Type of dance)
B A L L E T

TROAC
(Pretending professional)
A C T O R

Answers

Page 44
Tools

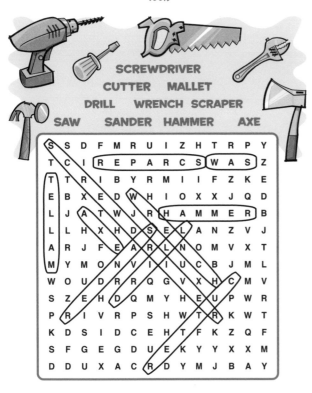

SCREWDRIVER
CUTTER   MALLET
DRILL   WRENCH   SCRAPER
SAW   SANDER   HAMMER   AXE

```
S S D F M R U I Z H T R P Y
T C I R E P A R C S W A S Z
T T R I B Y R M I I F Z K E
E B X E D W H I O X X J Q D
L J A T W J R H A M M E R B
L L H X H D S E L A N Z V J
A R J F E A R L N O M V X T
M Y M O N V I I U C B J M L
W O U D R R Q G V X H C M V
S Z E H D Q M Y H E U P W R
P R I V R P S H W T R K W T
K D S I D C E H T F K Z Q F
S F G E G D U E K Y Y X X M
D D U X A C R D Y M J B A Y
```

Page 45
Running Errands

IMOMMOMNMOMEMOMEMOM
DMOMMOMTOMOMGOMOM
MOMTOMOMTMOMHMOMMOM
EMOMPMOMOMOMTMOMTMOMY!

I
NEED
TO
GO
TO
THE
POTTY!

Page 46
Summer Fun

Page 47
Decode-a-Riddle

1=A	8=H	15=O	22=V
2=B	9=I	16=P	23=W
3=C	10=J	17=Q	24=X
4=D	11=K	18=R	25=Y
5=E	12=L	19=S	26=Z
6=F	13=M	20=T	21=U
7=G	14=N		

WHAT   CAN
23 8 1 20   3 1 14

YOU   KEEP
25 15 21   11 5 5 16

AFTER   YOU
1 6 20 5 18   25 15 21

GIVE   IT   TO
7 9 22 5   9 20   20 15

SOMEONE   ELSE?
19 15 13 5 15 14 5   5 12 19 5

YOUR   WORD
25 15 21 18   23 15 18 4

242

Answers

Page 48
Double Bananas

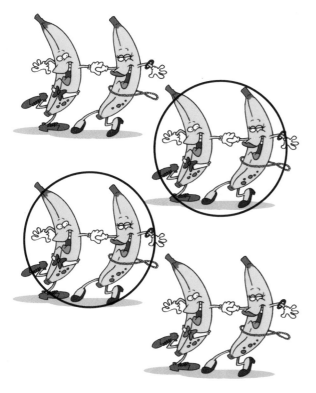

Page 49
Agriculture

AGRICULTURE

Here are just a few:

ace	culture	lace	rice
acre	cure	large	rule
age	ear	late	tag
agile	eat	leg	tail
alert	gate	liter	tale
argue	girl	race	tea
cage	glare	rag	teal
car	grail	rage	tear
cat	great	rail	tie
clear	guitar	rate	tiger
cruel	ice	real	urge

Page 50
Shark Maze

Page 51
Animals

Answers

Page 52
Camera Parts

FILM   BATTERIES
LENS   STRAP
SHUTTER   BODY
MOUNT   LEVER
FLASH   VIEWFINDER

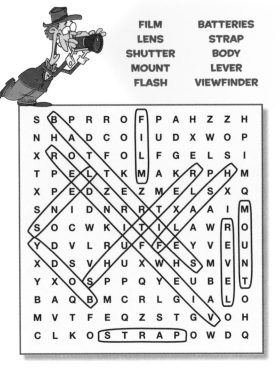

Page 53
Team Time

ACROSS
3 Oakland baseball team
6 Atlanta hockey team
8 Cleveland basketball team
9 St. Louis baseball team
10 LA baseball team

DOWN
1 New York football team
2 Toronto hockey team
4 Dallas football team
5 Boston basketball team
7 New England football team

Page 54
Wonderful Wizards

Page 55
Sudoku

4	2	9	3	7	1	8	5	6
6	5	8	4	2	9	7	1	3
1	7	3	5	6	8	2	9	4
2	8	6	9	5	7	3	4	1
7	9	1	2	4	3	5	6	8
5	3	4	1	8	6	9	7	2
3	6	2	7	9	4	1	8	5
8	1	7	6	3	5	4	2	9
9	4	5	8	1	2	6	3	7

Answers

Page 56
Sticky Stuff

P E A N U T
B U T T E R
S A N D W I C H

Page 57
Word Scramble

TRENASTUAR
(Eating place)

R E S T A U R A N T

CTYDNRIIAO
(Word describer)

D I C T I O N A R Y

RHCYISMTE
(Class subject)

C H E M I S T R Y

RELIOPCHET
(Aircraft)

H E L I C O P T E R

RPNEAAIL
(Sky coach)

A I R P L A N E

LABLSBAE
(Throwing game)

B A S E B A L L

SMULCE
(Under your skin)

M U S C L E

OOIUYSLLQ
(Singly speaking)

S O L I L O Q U Y

Page 58
Types of Dance

BALLROOM   BALLET
FOLK   TANGO
MODERN   JAZZ
POLKA   TAP
SALSA   SQUARE

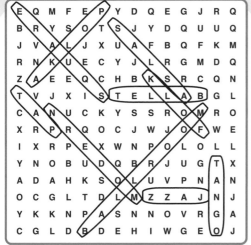

Page 59
Word Game

GIGINGIG

I N   B E T W E E N
G I G S

Answers

Page 60
Yummy!

ACROSS
4 Fresh and natural
6 Eat it at your birthday party
7 Frozen sweet treat
9 Thick and chocolaty
10 Liquid ice-cream drink

DOWN
1 Baked chocolate squares
2 Apple, pumpkin, chocolate cream
3 Lots in a box
5 Soft and sweet, chocolate or butterscotch
8 Drink it with cookies

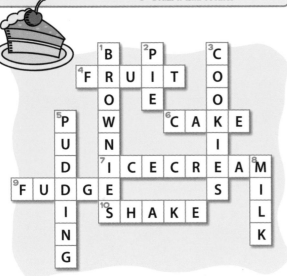

Page 61
Decode-a-Riddle

A=2	H=16	O=13	T=3
C=12	I=7	P=5	U=8
D=4	M=15	R=6	W=14
E=10	N=9	S=11	Y=1

WHEN YOU WISH
14 16 10 9   1 13 8   14 7 11 16

UPON A STAR,
8 5 13 9   2   11 3 2 6

YOUR DREAMS
1 13 8 6   4 6 10 2 15 11

COME TRUE.
12 13 15 10   3 6 8 10

Page 62
Double Ladybugs

Page 63
Engagement

ENGAGEMENT

Here are just a few:

age	man	name
ant	mane	neat
ate	mat	net
eat	mate	tag
egg	me	tame
gag	mean	tan
gage	meat	tea
game	meet	team
gate	mega	tee
gem	men	teen
gene	met	teenage
gnat	nag	ten

Answers

Page 64
Even Bear Maze

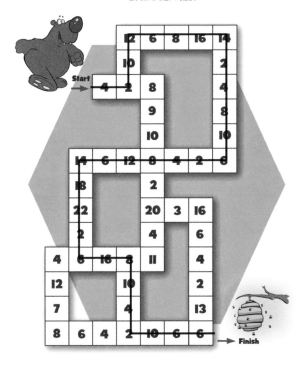

Page 65
Vehicle Sounds

```
        3W              4H
1C H O O C H O O N K
   I                    O
   R                    N
2C R U N C H            K
```

Page 66
Mythical Animal

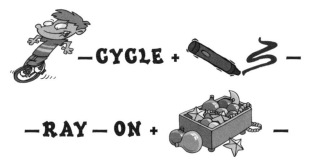

-CYCLE + ✎ ⌇ -

-RAY - ON + 🧸 -

-A - MENT

U N I C O R N

Page 67
Double Dinosaurs

Answers

Page 68
Safari Trip

Page 69

Page 70
Airplanes

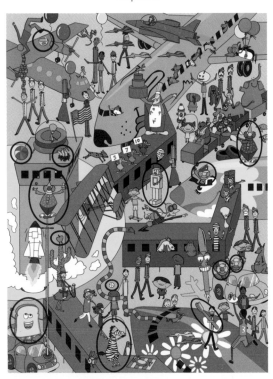

Page 71
Word Scramble

TNCFORON
(Face up against)

C O N F R O N T

LEGRAYL
(Place where art is shown)

G A L L E R Y

TANGINMAIOI
(Creative thinking)

I M A G I N A T I O N

CATINTRATO
(Appeal, pull)

A T T R A C T I O N

CIVDEENE
(Proof)

E V I D E N C E

DUNHATE
(Filled with ghosts)

H A U N T E D

GAGUNALE
(Word of a country)

L A N G U A G E

JASMAAP
(What you wear to bed)

P A J A M A S

Answers

Page 72
Fish

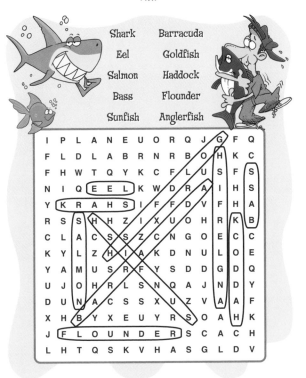

Shark   Barracuda

Eel   Goldfish

Salmon   Haddock

Bass   Flounder

Sunfish   Anglerfish

Page 73
Sudoku

8	9	5	7	3	6	2	4	1
1	7	2	5	9	4	3	6	8
4	6	3	1	2	8	9	5	7
2	5	1	4	6	3	8	7	9
9	3	4	8	5	7	1	2	6
7	8	6	2	1	9	5	3	4
6	1	8	3	7	5	4	9	2
5	4	7	9	8	2	6	1	3
3	2	9	6	4	1	7	8	5

Page 74
Thirsty

ACROSS
4 Clear and simple
5 Grind and brew
6 Sweet and bubbly
8 To gulp down

DOWN
1 Brewed from a bag
2 From fruit
3 Made with lemons
7 Good with chocolate

Across: 4 WATER, 5 COFFEE, 6 SODA, 8 DRINK
Down: 1 TEA, 2 JUICE, 3 LEMONADE, 7 MILK

Page 75
Decode-a-Message

A=4   H=3   T=2
C=1   O=5

H O T
3   5   2

C O C O A
1   5   1   5   4

Answers

Page 76
Word Game

T O O   M A N Y

C O O K S   I N   T H E

K I T C H E N

Page 77
Burglarize

BURGLARIZE

Here are just a few:

air	gab	large	real
argue	gear	leg	rear
bag	gel	liar	regal
bar	girl	lie	rib
barrel	glare	lug	rub
bear	grail	luge	rug
bizarre	grub	lure	rural
blare	gruel	rage	urge
blaze	ire	rail	zag
ear	lab	rale	zeal
err	lag	rare	zig

Page 78
Lucky Number Two

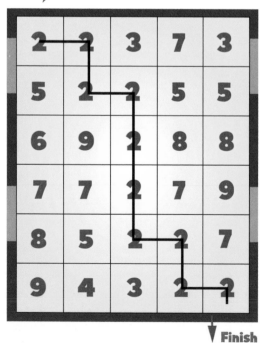

Page 79
State Capitals

Answers

Page 80
Wet Adventure

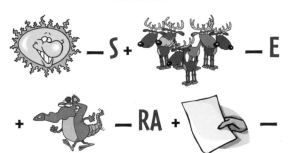

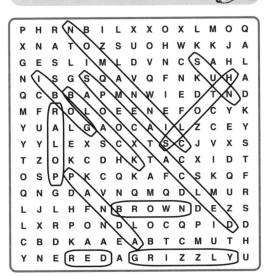

U N D E R
T H E
S E A

Page 81
Opposites Attract

1) DARK _____   4) SMALL _____

2) OLD _____   5) SHALLOW _____

3) ENEMIES _____   6) DRY _____

1. L I G H T
2. N E W
3. F R I E N D S
4. B I G
5. D E E P
6. W E T

Page 82
Types of Bears

Black   Panda   Polar
Cinnamon   Sloth
Gobi   Spectacled
Brown   Sun
Red   Grizzly

```
P H R N B I L X X O X L M O Q
X N A T O Z S U O H W K K J A
G E S L I M L D V N C S A H L
N I S G S Q A V Q F N K U H A
Q C B B A P M N W I E D T N D
M F R O L O E E N E F O C Y K
Y U A L G A O C A I L Z C E Y
Y Y L E X S C X T S C J V X S
T Z O K C D H K T A C X I D T
O S P P K C Q K A F C S K Q F
Q N G D A V N Q M Q D L M U R
L J L H F N B R O W N D E Z S
L X R P O N D L O C Q P I D D
C B D K A A A E A B T C M U T H
Y N E R E D A G R I Z Z L Y U
```

Page 83
Sudoku

6	5	9	4	1	8	2	3	7
8	7	3	2	6	5	1	9	4
1	4	2	9	7	3	6	5	8
5	8	4	7	2	9	3	6	1
2	9	6	3	4	1	7	8	5
3	1	7	5	8	6	9	4	2
7	2	5	6	3	4	8	1	9
9	6	1	8	5	2	4	7	3
4	3	8	1	9	7	5	2	6

Answers

Page 84
Carnival Fun

Page 85
Word Scramble

TEGILINNS
(Paying attention to)
L I S T E N I N G

YERVNOEE
(All the people)
E V E R Y O N E

RATHEFES
(On a bird)
F E A T H E R S

GIPVIRLEE
(Advantage, special treatment)
P R I V I L E G E

GALMENGI
(Shining)
G L E A M I N G

SELNERLETS
(Persistant, not stopping)
R E L E N T L E S S

PIWRESH
(Speak softly)
W H I S P E R

KRADYABC
(Behind the house)
B A C K Y A R D

Page 86
Bicycle Ride

Helmet   Pump
Chain   Lock
Gloves   Incline
Shoes   Bell
Tire   Handlebar

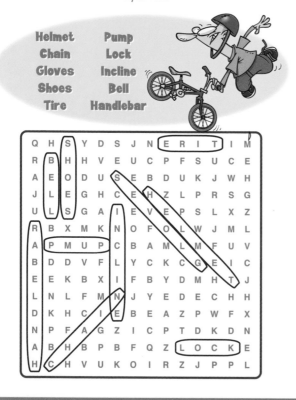

Page 87
Let's Build

ACROSS
1 MTUKCUPDR
  DUMP TRUCK
2 XVTREAAOC
  EXCAVATOR

DOWN
1 GGREDI
  DIGGER
3 XRMEI
  MIXER
4 LLREUBZDO
  BULLDOZER
5 TKFFLKOIR
  FORKLIFT

Answers

Page 88
Game Time

across		DOWN	
1	Kings and queens	2	Find the missing item.
5	Toss a ball back and forth.	3	Ready or not, here I come.
8	Hand off the baton	4	Spin the rope, jump
9	Card game with bids	5	Jump my piece.
10	Three water birds	6	You're it!
11	Two hands, no tackling	7	Small glass balls

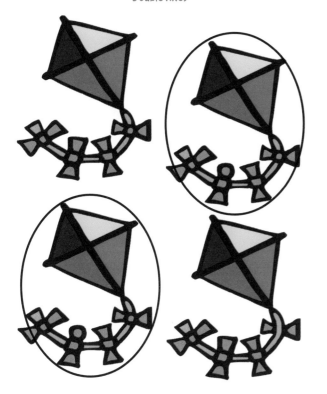

The crossword solution reads:
CHESS / CATCH across the top, SCAVENGERHUNT, HIDEANDSEE, JUMPROPE, CHECKERS down, RELAYRACE, MARBLES, BRIDGE, DUCKDUCKGOOSE, TOUCHFOOTBALL

Page 89
Lunchtime

A=8	F=16	K=9	R=10
B=14	G=1	M=15	S=6
C=11	H=5	N=7	T=12
E=4	I=2	O=3	W=13

GONE FISHING,
1 3 7 4 16 2 6 5 2 7 1

BACK TOMORROW.
14 8 11 9 12 3 15 3 10 10 3 13

Page 90
Double Kites

Page 91
Anatomical

ANATOMICAL

Here are just a few:

act	clot	loan	not
action	coal	loin	oat
ail	coat	lot	oil
aim	coil	mail	oilcan
ant	icon	main	on
atom	into	malt	tan
calm	ion	man	tic
can	lima	mania	ton
canal	limo	mic	tonic
clam	lint	mint	
clan	lit	molt	

Answers

Page 92
Odd House Maze

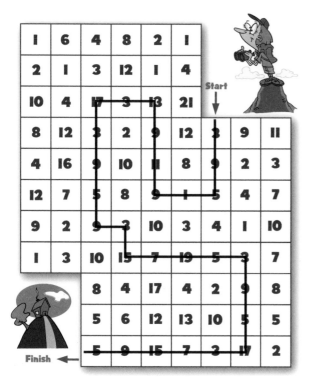

Page 93
Under the Sea

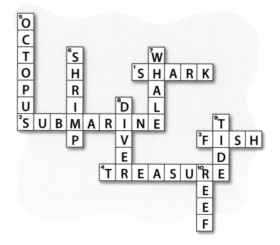

Page 94
On the Go

— REE + — — DROPS + — S + — N

T R A I N
T I C K E T

Page 95
Sudoku

2	3	9	5	8	1	7	4	6
6	4	7	9	2	3	1	5	8
8	1	5	6	4	7	9	3	2
7	5	3	2	1	6	4	8	9
9	8	2	7	5	4	6	1	3
4	6	1	8	3	9	5	2	7
1	9	8	4	7	2	3	6	5
3	2	6	1	9	5	8	7	4
5	7	4	3	6	8	2	9	1

Answers

Page 96
Ice Hockey Game

Page 97

Page 98
Traveling Circus

Page 99
Word Scramble

ACPEH
(Juicy summer fruit)

P E A C H

SHUP
(To shove)

P U S H

POTS
(Halt, cease)

S T O P

PLHE
(Assist)

H E L P

ROYRW
(To fret, be concerned)

W O R R Y

ARHI
(It's on your head)

H A I R

GTHIL
(Bright, glowing bulb)

L I G H T

UHTTR
(Honestly)

T R U T H

Answers

Page 100
Car Parts

Tailgate	Brakes
Bumper	Horn
Tire	Grille
Dashboard	Hubcap
Engine	Exhaust pipe

Page 101
Sudoku

6	2	4	5	7	8	9	1	3
1	9	7	3	6	4	8	5	2
5	3	8	2	9	1	6	7	4
2	8	5	9	4	7	3	6	1
4	7	9	1	3	6	5	2	8
3	6	1	8	5	2	7	4	9
8	1	3	6	2	5	4	9	7
7	5	2	4	8	9	1	3	6
9	4	6	7	1	3	2	8	5

Page 102
Authors

ACROSS
1. ___ Christian Anderson
2. ___ Kipling
3. ___ Dickens
4. ___ Shelley
5. ___ Austen

DOWN
1. ___ Melville
2. ___ Waldo Emerson
5. ___ London
6. ___ Carroll
7. ___ Hodgson Burnett

Crossword answers: LEWIS, HANS, FRANCES, RUDYARD, HERMAN, CHARLES, RALPH, MARY, JANE, JACK

Page 103
Decode-a-Message

A=4	I=8	S=2
B=1	M=9	T=5
E=6	O=3	Y=7

B A B Y
1 4 1 7

B O T T O M S
1 3 5 5 3 9 2

Answers

Page 104
Double Aliens

Page 105
Influenza

INFLUENZA

Here are just a few:

ail	fin	fun	life
alien	final	funnel	line
elf	finale	inn	linen
fail	fine	lane	nail
fan	flan	leaf	nil
fez	flea	lean	nine
fie	flu	lie	nun
file	fuel	lieu	zeal

Page 106
Shopping Time

Page 107
I'm Hungry

Answers

Page 108
Dangerous Weather

GON + R +  9 0 – ETY + G

<u>T O R N A D O</u>

<u>W A R N I N G</u>

Page 109
Class Schedule

Crossword solution:

- GEOGRAPHY
- ENGLISH
- HISTORY
- ART
- CHEMISTRY
- MATH
- STORY

Page 110
Beach Time

Lotion   Swimsuit
Sand   Waves
Ocean   Shovel
Chair   Swimming
Umbrella Surfing

Word search grid:

```
W A G V U M B R E L L A W A
O R N A Q H F Y T S S U M Y
V O S I M P I K L W C U V D B
O Y H N J B J Q I F E M R J U
Y I O M Y I A M Q N L K U X H
R A M I P A S R B O A L D U C
I H I E W V U K Y T T B E M C
A C S L S I Q W I R J R B C X B
H B T Z X O A N D P B Q O J
C P O G N Q R V X N P T W R
B X R G K M P L E K A T Y G
L C P F N A M A U S U S Q K
S U R F I N G G J S I B B G
X K P A S H W O T G A A O X
```

Page 111
Sudoku

7	4	1	9	8	2	3	6	5
5	9	6	4	3	1	7	2	8
8	3	2	5	7	6	9	4	1
3	6	5	8	4	9	1	7	2
1	8	9	7	2	5	6	3	4
4	2	7	6	1	3	8	5	9
9	5	4	3	6	8	2	1	7
2	7	3	1	9	4	5	8	6
6	1	8	2	5	7	4	9	3

Answers

Page 112
Dino Paradise

Page 113
Word Scramble

VDOE
(Bird of peace)
D O V E

HCSOK
(Surprise, stun)
S H O C K

KACP
(Put into a suitcase)
P A C K

PLIF
(Turn over)
F L I P

HWOS
(Performance)
S H O W

LADE
(Hand out cards)
D E A L

KRWO
(Do a job)
W O R K

IJNO
(Become part of a club or team)
J O I N

Page 114
Types of Birds

Mockingbird   Wren
Heron   Sparrow
Hummingbird   Woodpecker
Shorebird   Warbler
Bluebird   Duck

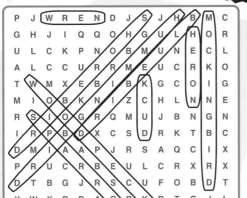

```
P  J  W  R  E  N  D  J  S  J  H  B  M  C
G  H  J  I  Q  Q  O  H  G  U  L  H  O  R
U  L  C  K  P  N  O  B  M  U  N  E  C  L
A  L  C  C  U  R  R  M  E  U  C  R  K  O
T  W  M  X  E  B  I  B  K  G  C  O  I  G
M  I  O  B  K  N  I  Z  C  H  L  N  N  E
R  S  O  G  R  Q  M  U  U  D  R  K  G  N
I  R  P  B  D  X  C  S  D  R  K  T  B  C
D  M  I  A  A  P  J  R  S  A  Q  C  I  X
P  R  U  C  R  B  E  U  L  C  R  X  R  X
D  T  B  G  J  R  S  C  U  F  O  B  D  T
Y  W  X  R  D  A  O  R  K  D  T  C  J  L
Y  O  R  E  L  Q  J  W  M  E  S  O  X  D
N  G  M  R  E  L  B  R  A  W  R  T  V  K
```

Page 115
Militaristic

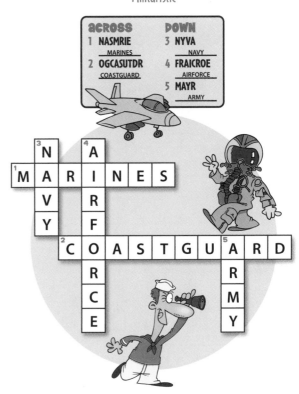

ACROSS
1 NASMRIE — MARINES
2 OGCASUTDR — COASTGUARD

DOWN
3 NYVA — NAVY
4 FRAICROE — AIRFORCE
5 MAYR — ARMY

Crossword grid:
- 3 Down: N A V Y
- 1 Across: M A R I N E S
- 4 Down: A I R F O R C E
- 2 Across: C O A S T G U A R D
- 5 Down: A R M Y

Answers

Page 116
Musical Instruments

across
4 Long, silver woodwind instrument
5 Woodwind instrument that sounds like a duck
6 Jazz instrument with a double reed

DOWN
1 Biggest baritone brass instrument
2 Second largest, upright orchestra instrument
3 Highest pitched band instrument

Page 117
Decode-a-Message

A=2	G=1	M=3	O=6	T=5
D=7	H=4	N=10	R=11	W=9
E=12	I=8			Y=13

H A I R   T O D A Y ,
4 2 8 11   5 6 7 2 13

G O N E
1 6 10 12

T O M O R R O W .
5 6 3 6 11 11 6 9

Page 118
Double Skydiver

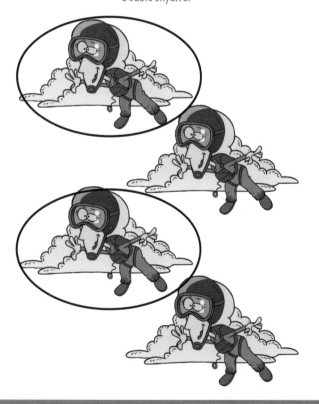

Page 119
Veterinarian

VETERINARIAN

Here are just a few:

air	even	nerve	river
ant	event	net	tan
art	ever	never	tea
ate	inn	nine	tear
avert	inner	ran	tee
ear	invent	rant	ten
eat	invert	rare	tiara
enter	invite	rat	train
entire	irate	rate	trivia
era	near	rear	vain
eve	neat	rent	vine

Answers

Page 120
Even Plane Maze

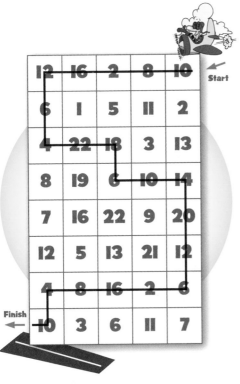

Page 121
What Time Is It?

Page 122
Fun For All

— GA — PHONE

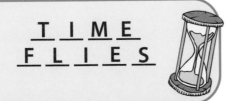

T I M E
F L I E S

Page 123
Double Apples

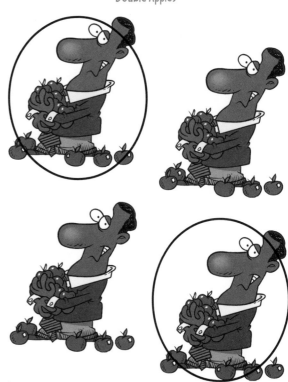

Answers

Page 124
Pretty Peacocks

Page 125

Page 126
Pyramids

Page 127
Word Scramble

VAERBEEG
(Thirst quencher)
B E V E R A G E

REOEIHN
(Female hero)
H E R O I N E

YSYSEDO
(Epic journey)
O D Y S S E Y

BHRMAUEGR
(Goes with fries)
H A M B U R G E R

GIISHATNKGVN
(Holiday)
T H A N K S G I V I N G

OEOTCSINRNVA
(Long chat)
C O N V E R S A T I O N

ELADTOR
(Ballerina wear)
L E O T A R D

OGBIWLN
(Rolling game)
B O W L I N G

Answers

Page 128
Healthy Food

FRUIT   WHOLE GRAIN
VEGETABLES   RAISINS
BEANS   GRANOLA
FIBER   YOGURT
NUTS   CHICKEN

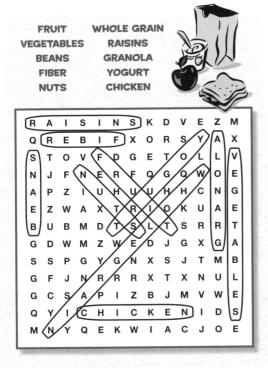

```
R A I S I N S K D V E Z M
Q R E B I F X O R S Y A X
S T O V F D G E T O L L V
N J F N E R F O G Q W O E
A P Z I U H U U H C N G
E Z W A X T R I O K U A E
B U B M D T S L T S R R T
G D W M Z W E D J G X G A
S S P G Y G N X S J T M B
G F J N R R R X T X N U L
G C S A P I Z B J M V W E
Q Y I C H I C K E N I W S
M N Y Q E K W I A C J O E
```

Page 129
Sudoku

3	2	1	4	9	5	8	6	7
6	8	4	2	7	1	9	5	3
9	7	5	3	8	6	2	1	4
4	9	6	7	1	3	5	2	8
7	5	2	8	6	4	1	3	9
1	3	8	5	2	9	7	4	6
5	6	7	1	3	8	4	9	2
8	1	9	6	4	2	3	7	5
2	4	3	9	5	7	6	8	1

Page 130
Building a House

ACROSS
2 Outdoor room
4 Cover it all
6 Cover the walls and floor
9 Lowest level
10 Keep you warm
11 Hang out
12 Open, close, see through

DOWN
1 Walk right through
3 Separates rooms
5 Cook up a meal
7 Cover the roof
8 Where people sleep

Crossword answers:
- 2 PORCH
- 4 ROOF
- 6 TILES
- 9 BASEMENT
- 10 FURNACE
- 11 LIVINGROOM
- 12 WINDOWS
- 1 DOORWAY
- 3 WALL
- 5 ... BEDROOM
- 7 SHINGLES
- 8 KITCHEN

Page 131
Decode-a-Riddle

A=!	H=*	O=>	V=?
B=@	I=(	P=[	W=/
C=#	J=+	Q=]	X=\
D=$	K=)	R="	Y=}
E=%	L=;	S="	Z={
F=^	M=:	T=`	
G=&	N=<	U='	

WHAT IS AN

ORANGUTAN'S

FAVORITE TOOL?

A MONKEY

WRENCH

263

Answers

Page 132
Animal Habitat

Page 133
Dinnertime

DINNERTIME

Here are just a few:

deem	ere	nine	tie
deer	indent	red	tier
den	item	rent	time
denim	mend	ride	timer
dent	mere	rind	timid
die	merit	rite	tin
dim	met	tee	tire
dime	meter	ten	tired
dine	mite	tend	tree
dinner	nerd	tender	trend
enter	net	term	tried

Page 134
A-maze-ing Ray

Page 135
In the Cupboard

Answers

Page 136
Name of a Leader

P R E S I D E N T

Page 137
School Bus

Page 138
Track and Field

Running   Endurance
Hurdle   Relay
Start   Interval
Finish   Spikes
Crossbar   Training

```
O R D M I O C J L G K Y T E
T E I H Z N T K N N L W R J
U L U P C B T I X S X K W B
S A E D I O N E T Z M L H E
E Y A U J I B A R X R M V G
Y N T C A D R B P V H G L C
R Z D R L T S J R G A O I L
U L T U E L D R U H K L C T
N N N D R S P I K E S F J X
N L W T N A Y V X X J L W M
I E Z Z K S N F Q Y B D L V
N F I N I S H C H M K J A T
G M P A I O P D E R A M I N
N L R A B S S O R C U E E S
```

Page 139
More State Capitals

across
2 Texas
6 Georgia
8 Oregon
10 Idaho

DOWN
1 Alaska
3 Kansas
4 Ohio
5 Michigan
7 New York
9 Delaware

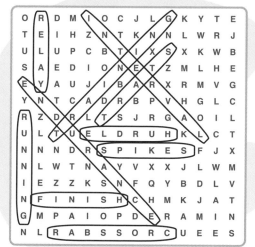

Answers

Page 140
Lemonade Stand

Page 141
Word Scramble

SOGOE
(Bird)

G O O S E

JNUAC
(Spicy style)

C A J U N

YDINW
(Air moving)

W I N D Y

BITRBA
(Twitchy animal)

R A B B I T

TRAGUI
(Instrument)

G U I T A R

EHUSO
(Dwelling)

H O U S E

Page 142
Classic Books

Pinocchio
The Wizard of Oz
Little Women
Black Beauty
Treasure Island

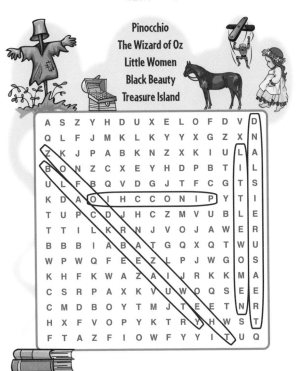

Page 143
Sudoku

8	4	2	9	5	3	6	1	7
7	1	9	2	8	6	5	3	4
6	5	3	7	1	4	9	8	2
3	8	1	5	7	2	4	9	6
2	6	4	3	9	8	7	5	1
9	7	5	6	4	1	3	2	8
1	9	6	4	2	5	8	7	3
4	2	7	8	3	9	1	6	5
5	3	8	1	6	7	2	4	9

Answers

Page 144
Time To Laugh

ACROSS
2 Little laugh
7 ____ — ____ who's there?
8 Silly questions and answers

DOWN
1 Show your teeth.
3 Animated shows
4 In the circus
5 Stand-up guy
6 Tell me funny ones.

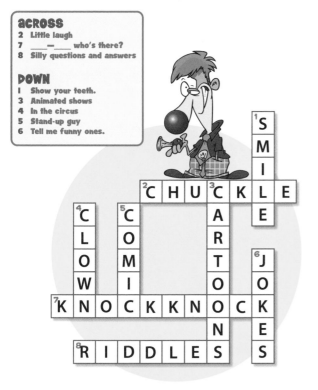

Crossword solution:

1. SMILE
2. CHUCKLE
4. CLOWN
5. COMIC
3. CARTOONS
6. JOKES
7. KNOCK KNOCK
8. RIDDLES

Page 145
Decode-a-Message

A=6	G=10	N=1	T=4
D=2	H=3	O=7	U=11
E=8	I=5	R=14	
F=13	L=12	S=9	

END OF THE TUNNEL

```
T   H   E   R   E        I   S        A
4   3   8   14  8        5   9        6

L   I   G   H   T        A   T        T   H   E
12  5   10  3   4        6   4        4   3   8

E   N   D        O   F        T   H   E
8   1   2        7   13       4   3   8

T   U   N   N   E   L  .
4   11  1   1   8   12
```

Page 146
Double Cats

Page 147
Alphabet Soup

ALPHABET SOUP

Here are just a few:

able	bet	hut	pale
about	blast	lab	paste
alas	bloat	last	pat
aloe	blue	lash	path
also	boast	leash	pause
ape	halo	let	petal
ate	hate	lost	plate
bate	help	lush	plus
bash	hole	oat	salt
bath	hose	oath	sea
beast	host	out	seat

Answers

Page 148
Lucky Number 18

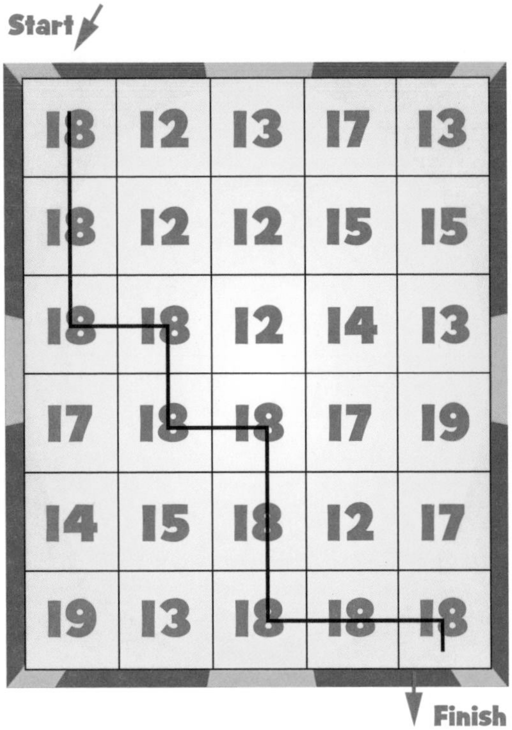
Start
18 12 13 17 13
18 12 12 15 15
18 18 12 14 13
17 18 18 17 19
14 15 18 12 17
19 13 18 18 18
Finish

Page 149
Sudoku

3	2	4	1
1	4	2	3
2	1	3	4
4	3	1	2

Page 150
Small Pet

—PS +
—
—EBRA +
—M +
— OG

L I Z A R D

Page 151
Scientific

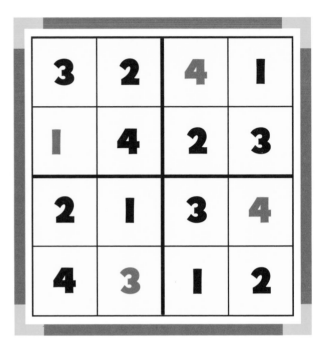

SCIENTIFIC

Here are just a few:

cent	ice	nice	since
cite	infect	nit	sit
cities	infest	nite	site
fin	insect	scenic	ten
fine	inset	scent	tic
finest	its	sect	tie
fist	nest	sent	tin
fit	net	sin	

Answers

Page 152
A Pirate's Life

Page 153

Page 154
Funny Farm

Page 155
Library Number

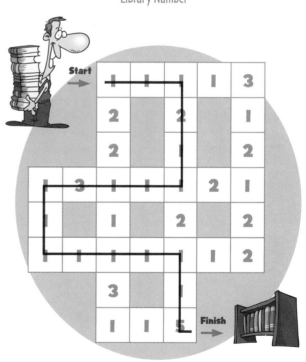

Answers

Page 156
Ocean Wildlife

Fish	Otter
Shark	Sea Turtle
Dolphin	Starfish
Whale	Oysters
Seal	Clams

Page 157
Multiplication Tables

across	DOWN
1 6 x 3 = 18	1 40 x 2 = 80
2 9 x 1 = 9	3 4 x 5 = 20

1 EIGHTEEN (across), with EIGHTY down
3 TWENTY (down)
2 NINE (across)

Page 158
Read All About It

across
3 Pictures and words
6 Out every day
7 Write it for school
9 Rhymes sometimes
10 Performed on a stage

DOWN
1 Weekly or monthly
2 Between two covers
4 Read it on screen
5 Small tale
8 Full-length fiction book

1 MAGAZINE
2 BOOK
3 COMIC
4 COMPUTER
5 SHORT STORY
6 NEWSPAPER
7 REPORTER
8 NOVEL
9 POETRY
10 PLAY

Page 159
Decode-a-Riddle

A=Z	I=R	Q=J	Y=B	*=7
B=Y	J=Q	R=I	Z=A	#=8
C=X	K=P	S=H	!=I	>=9
D=W	L=O	T=G	@=2	+=0
E=V	M=N	U=F	<=3
F=U	N=M	V=E	$=4
G=T	O=L	W=D	%=5
H=S	P=K	X=C	&=6

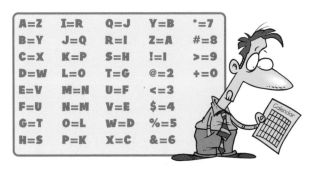

WHICH MONTH
D S R X S   N L M G S

HAS 2 8 DAYS
S Z H @ # W Z B H

IN IT?
R M R G

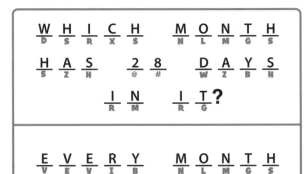

EVERY MONTH
V E V I B   N L M G S

Answers

Page 160
Double Gumballs

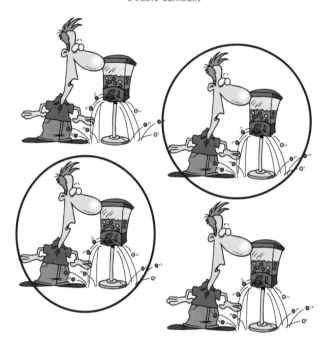

Page 161
Rattlesnake

RATTLESNAKE

Here are just a few:

alas	easel	lease	reek
alert	eternal	nasal	rest
alter	kate	near	salt
ankle	karate	neat	sank
area	knee	nest	sea
ark	kettle	rake	sear
art	knelt	rank	sleek
ask	lark	rant	snare
eat	laser	rate	state
earn	latter	rattle	take
ease	learn	reel	treat

Page 162
Alien Odd Maze

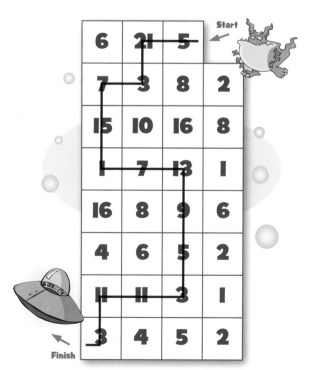

Page 163
Post Office

Answers

Page 164
Type of Book

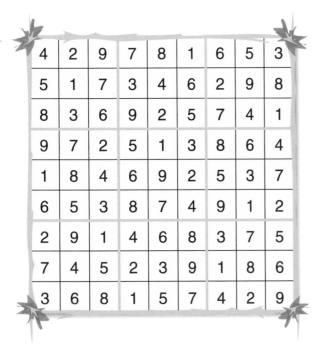

D I C T I O N A R Y

Page 165
Farm Animals

PIG   COW
HORSE   GOAT
SHEEP   DUCK
ROOSTER   GEESE
CHICKEN   DOG

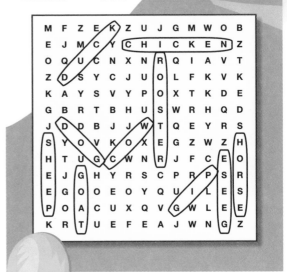

Page 166
Sudoku

4	2	9	7	8	1	6	5	3
5	1	7	3	4	6	2	9	8
8	3	6	9	2	5	7	4	1
9	7	2	5	1	3	8	6	4
1	8	4	6	9	2	5	3	7
6	5	3	8	7	4	9	1	2
2	9	1	4	6	8	3	7	5
7	4	5	2	3	9	1	8	6
3	6	8	1	5	7	4	2	9

Page 167
Double Builders

Answers

Page 168
Hockey Rink

Page 169
Word Scramble

WRAD
(Create a picture)

D R A W

ETEHT
(They are in your mouth)

T E E T H

KAFE
(Not real)

F A K E

PALEP
(Round, red fruit)

A P P L E

ESMRG
(They cause sickness)

G E R M S

NISGW
(Go back and forth)

S W I N G

LMKI
(Drink it with cookies)

M I L K

DOCL
(Chilly, freezing)

C O L D

Page 170
Jungle Animals

LION   CROCODILE
ZEBRA   LIZARD
ELEPHANT   WOLF
BABOON   JAGUAR
CHEETAH   COUGAR

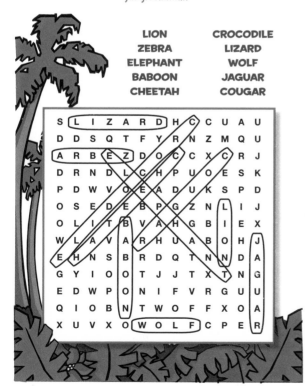

Page 171
Sudoku

8	3	1	7	6	4	2	9	5
7	9	6	2	5	8	1	3	4
4	2	5	1	3	9	6	7	8
3	4	9	8	2	5	7	6	1
6	8	7	3	9	1	4	5	2
1	5	2	4	7	6	3	8	9
5	1	4	6	8	7	9	2	3
9	7	3	5	1	2	8	4	6
2	6	8	9	4	3	5	1	7

Answers

Page 172
Autumn

across
1. The air gets ___ .
4. There is less and less _____ .
5. The trees get ___ .
6. Brightly colored leaves
7. Orange vegetables that can be carved
8. Put away light jackets, put on _____
10. Gathering of crops
11. The season to prepare for _____

DOWN
2. What falls in autumn
3. Light up the ____ .
6. Another name for autumn
9. Can harm delicate plants

Crossword solution:
- 1 CHILLY
- 2 LEAVES (down)
- 3 FIREPLACE (down)
- DAYLIGHT
- 5 BARE
- 6 FOLIAGE
- FALL (down)
- 7 PUMPKINS
- WARMCOATS
- 9 FROST (down)
- 10 HARVEST
- WINTER

Page 173
Decode-a-Message

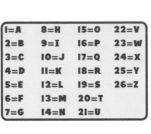

1=A	8=H	15=O	22=V
2=B	9=I	16=P	23=W
3=C	10=J	17=Q	24=X
4=D	11=K	18=R	25=Y
5=E	12=L	19=S	26=Z
6=F	13=M	20=T	
7=G	14=N	21=U	

C A T   I N   T R E E
3 1 20   9 14   20 18 5 5

I S   S A V E D   B Y
9 19   19 1 22 5 4   2 25

F I R E M A N!
6 9 18 5 13 1 14

Page 174
Double Jack-o'-lanterns

Page 175
Scatterbrain

SCATTERBRAIN

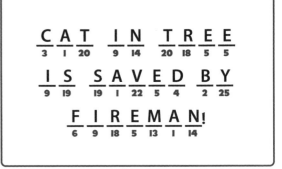

Here are just a few:

ace	bent	neat	saber
acne	bitter	nest	scab
air	cabin	net	scar
arena	can	race	since
art	case	rain	stab
attic	eat	raise	state
ban	ice	rant	tact
bane	insect	react	tar
bare	insert	rear	tart
batter	intact	rib	tent
beat	near	rice	tribe

274

Answers

Page 176
Even Maze

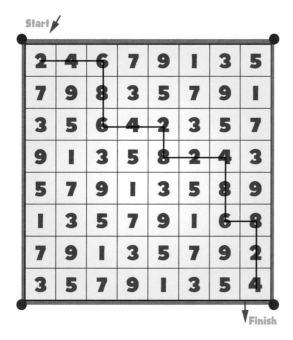

Start ↙

2	4	6	7	9	1	3	5
7	9	8	3	5	7	9	1
3	5	6	4	2	3	5	7
9	1	3	5	8	2	4	3
5	7	9	1	3	5	8	9
1	3	5	7	9	1	6	8
7	9	1	3	5	7	9	2
3	5	7	9	1	3	5	4

↓ Finish

Page 177
Types of Vegetables

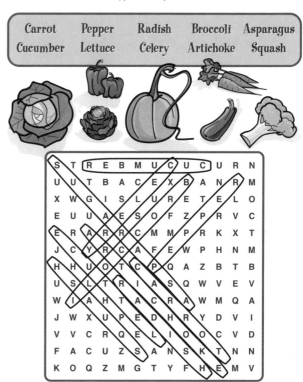

Carrot   Pepper   Radish   Broccoli   Asparagus
Cucumber   Lettuce   Celery   Artichoke   Squash

Page 178
Family

+ IS +

− AL + RE + −

− IMBL + +

− F − H

H O M E   I S
W H E R E   T H E
H E A R T   I S.

Page 179
Sudoku

7	6	3	2	5	9	4	1	8
4	1	2	7	3	8	5	6	9
5	9	8	1	6	4	2	3	7
6	5	7	8	4	3	1	9	2
3	2	9	5	7	1	8	4	6
8	4	1	6	9	2	7	5	3
1	8	5	9	2	6	3	7	4
2	3	6	4	1	7	9	8	5
9	7	4	3	8	5	6	2	1

Answers

Page 180
Can You Canoe?

Page 181

Page 182
Sky High Fun

Page 183
Word Scramble

EGOLV
(Hand warmer)

G L O V E

KJAC
(Tire fixer)

J A C K

SARM
(Planet)

M A R S

PAT
(Type of dance)

T A P

Answers

Page 184
Types of Dogs

Afghan   Havanese   Poodle
Beagle   Labrador   Weimaraner
Chihuahua   Maltese
Dalmatian
Greyhound

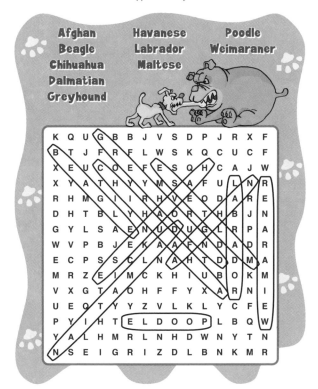

Page 185
Add It Up

across		DOWN	
1 9 + 8 = 17		1 24 + 36 = 60	
2 18 + 11 = 29		3 16 + 24 = 40	

SEVENTEEN
SIXTY
FORTY
TWENTYNINE

Page 186
Jigsaw Puzzle

JIGSAW PUZZLE

Here are just a few:

age	isle	page	sag
agile	jail	pail	sage
aisle	jaw	pale	saw
gap	jig	pause	sew
gape	jug	pea	size
gasp	lag	peal	sizzle
gauze	lap	pew	slug
gaze	lapse	pile	spa
gel	lie	pizza	spew
glue	lisp	plea	wasp
guzzle	luge	plug	wig

Page 187
Math Code

$7 - 5 + 1 = \boxed{3}$

$3 + 4 - 6 = \boxed{1}$

$10 \times 2 = \boxed{20}$

$5 + 6 + 8 = \boxed{19}$

1=A	2=B	3=C	4=D	5=E
6=F	7=G	8=H	9=I	10=J
11=K	12=L	13=M	14=N	15=O
16=P	17=Q	18=R	19=S	20=T
21=U	22=V	23=W	24=X	25=Y
26=Z				

C A T S

Answers

Page 188
Double Princesses

Page 189
Scary Stuff

across
4 Flying mammal
5 All bones
6 Spirit that lives on
7 Another word for spooky

DOWN
1 Living dead that feeds on blood
2 Spell caster
3 Inhuman creature

Page 190
Even Superhero

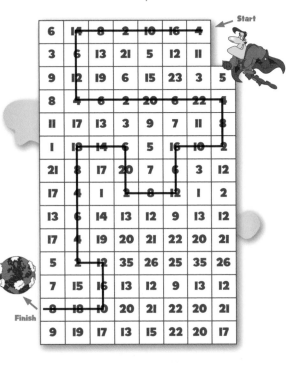

Page 191
Amusement Park

Guess your ___   Roller ___   ___-go-round   Fortune ___

Answers

Page 192
Ocean Life

C O R A L

R E E F

Page 193
Ice-Cream Stand

Page 194
Types of Cookies

Oatmeal   Snickerdoodle
Chocolate chip   Butter
Peanut butter   Gingersnap
Sugar   Linzer
Shortbread   Biscotti

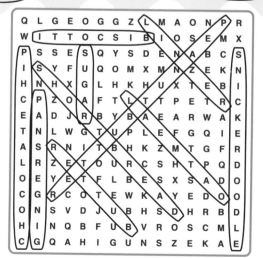

Page 195
Ready for Take-Off

across
1 Rest your head.
3 Lean against
7 Really fast plane
8 Put your food on
10 Where the pilot sits
11 Serves the food

down
1 Get on board the ___ .
2 Provides the power
4 What the pilots operate
5 Keeps you strapped in
6 It floats .
9 Flies the plane

Answers

Page 196
Jungle Jamboree

Page 197
Word Scramble

HTILG
(Brightens room)

L I G H T

PYPHA
(Emotion)

H A P P Y

LDOWR
(Where we live)

W O R L D

NKIG
(Ruler)

K I N G

Page 198
All-Star Hockey

Puck	Penalty
Pad	Interference
Assist	Overtime
Goalie	Rebound
Pass	Breakaway

```
B L O B I B N C M W M D S O
V P J E I X U C M K C U P P
E C N E R E F R E T N I L L
J P A S S Z W B U F E K G J
F H K G Z T P M Q Z P T R V
E Q A K Y A W A K A E R B E
K M A W D W B T D F B Q F Q
L Z I A R E B O U N D A L T
V B G T S N Y T L A N E P A
V R T O R S D C K A E W W Y
X R H Q A E I V S I C L J D
H I Z P F L V S X Q D V Q
L A R M F N I O T D D J S Z
W B M F E L S E U P N F M H
```

Page 199
Sudoku

1	5	6	8	3	7	9	2	4
9	7	3	6	2	4	8	1	5
4	2	8	9	1	5	6	7	3
8	9	5	2	7	3	4	6	1
3	1	7	4	9	6	5	8	2
2	6	4	5	8	1	7	3	9
5	8	2	1	6	9	3	4	7
6	3	9	7	4	2	1	5	8
7	4	1	3	5	8	2	9	6

Answers

Page 200
Flying Machines

across	DOWN
1 Presidential	6 Hot air
2 Outer space	7 Rotors
3 Wright brothers	8 Silent military
4 Commercial airliner	
5 Lands on water	

Crossword answers:
AIRFORCEONE
SHUTTLE
JETPLANE
BIPLANE
SEAPLANE
STEALTH
BALLOON
HELICOPTER

Page 201
Decode-a-Message

$(40 \div 2) + 2 = \boxed{22}$

$(4 \times 5) - 15 = \boxed{5}$

$(100 \div 10) + 4 = \boxed{14}$

$3 + 4 + 7 + 2 + 5 = \boxed{21}$

$(7 \times 3) - 2 = \boxed{19}$

1=A	2=B	3=C	4=D	5=E	6=F
7=G	8=H	9=I	10=J	11=K	12=L
13=M	14=N	15=O	16=P	17=Q	18=R
19=S	20=T	21=U	22=V	23=W	24=X
25=Y	26=Z				

V E N U S

Page 202
Cooking Utensils

Knife   Thermometer
Whisk   Masher
Spatula   Shredder
Scraper   Grater
Measuring cup Blender

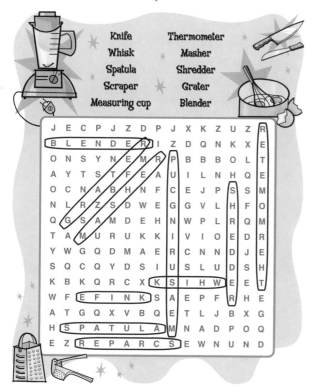

Page 203
Haunted House

HAUNTED HOUSE

Here are just a few:

and	dot	hunt	seat
ant	duo	hut	sedate
ash	east	note	set
aunt	eat	nude	shoe
auto	had	nut	shut
dash	hand	oat	snot
death	head	oath	snout
denote	heat	onset	tease
dense	hen	out	teen
dent	hose	saute	these
dose	host	sea	unease

Answers

Page 204
Lucky Number One

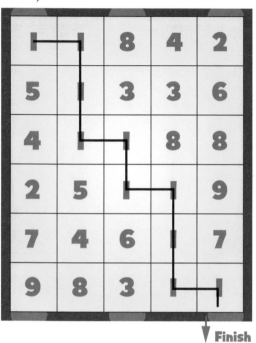

Start ↯

Finish ↓

Page 205
Time to Bake!

across
1 LNAVILA ___VANILLA___
2 GEG ___EGG___
3 LORUF ___FLOUR___
4 TRETBU ___BUTTER___

DOWN
5 KGBANI WOPEDR
___BAKING___ ___POWDER___
6 GUSRA ___SUGAR___

⁵B
¹VANILLA
A
K
I ⁶S
N U
²EGG G
P A
³FLOUR
W
D
E
⁴BUTTER

Page 206
Vehicle

+ — BA +

— DA — T + — D

F I R E
T R U C K

Page 207
Decode-a-Riddle

I=A	8=H	15=O	22=V
2=B	9=I	16=P	23=W
3=C	10=J	17=Q	24=X
4=D	II=K	18=R	25=Y
5=E	12=L	19=S	26=Z
6=F	13=M	20=T	
7=G	14=N	21=U	

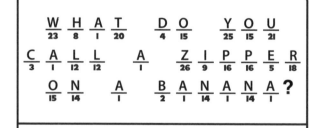

W H A T   D O   Y O U
23 8 1 20   4 15   25 15 21

C A L L   A   Z I P P E R
3 1 12 12   1   26 9 16 16 5 18

O N   A   B A N A N A?
15 14   1   2 1 14 1 14 1

A   F R U I T   F L Y
1   6 18 21 9 20   6 12 25

282

Answers

Page 208
One, Two, Three, Fore?

Page 209

Page 210
Pirates Ahoy!

Page 211
Water Maze

Answers

Page 212
Animals in Hibernation

BEAR · FROG · BAT · SQUIRREL · HEDGEHOG · RACCOON · SKUNK · CHIPMUNK · BADGER · HAMSTER

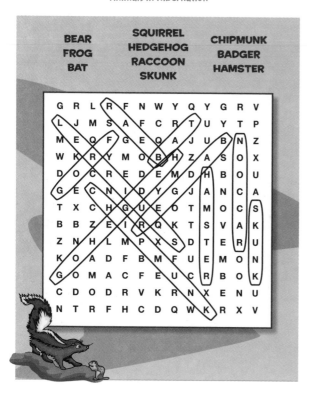

Page 213
Get to Work

across
1 ARDH RDVIE — HARD DRIVE
2 UOSME — MOUSE
3 MPERTUOC — COMPUTER

DOWN
2 NOIMROT — MONITOR
4 UORRET — ROUTER
5 ROABDYEK — KEYBOARD

Page 214
Down Under

across
3 Rock-like animals
7 Hard shells
9 They swim in schools.
10 Humans staying underwater

DOWN
1 Swimmers, beware!
2 Shocking!
4 Undersea vessel
5 Half-human creature of legend
6 Many legs
8 Green plantlife

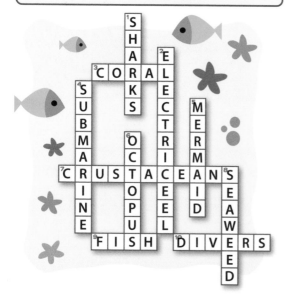

Page 215
Word Game

PENNY FOR YOUR THOUGHTS

Answers

Page 216
Road Signs

Speed Limit	Caution
Stop	Do Not Enter
Dead End	Yield
One Way	No Parking
Slow	Parking

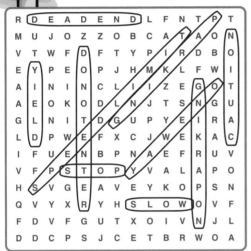

Page 217
Rollercoaster

ROLLERCOASTER

Here are just a few:

ace	cereal	lace	reel
acre	clear	lease	roast
act	close	leer	roll
all	coal	let	root
art	color	loser	sale
call	crate	lost	salt
caller	ear	oar	scale
case	ease	oat	tea
castle	east	race	tear
cat	eel	rare	trace
cello	era	real	troll

Page 218
Star Number Maze

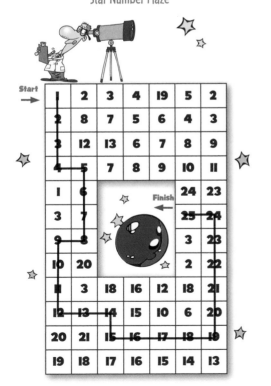

Page 219
Decode-a-Riddle

A=!	G=&	M=:	S="	X=\
B=@	H=*	N=<	T=´	Y=}
C=#	I=(	O=>	U='	Z={
D=$	J=+	P=[	V=?	
E=%	K=)	Q=]	W=/	
F=^	L=;	R="		

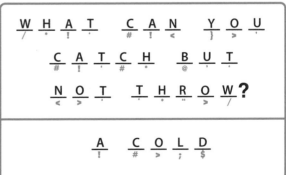

W H A T   C A N   Y O U

C A T C H   B U T

N O T   T H R O W?

A   C O L D

Answers

Page 220
Office Supplies

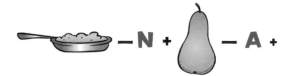 —N +  — A +

 —AT +  — ON

+  — ICKLE

<u>P A P E R</u>
<u>C L I P</u>

Page 221
Double Cellos

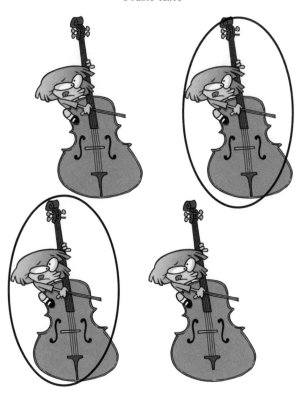

Page 222
Chess

Pawn   Knight
Bishop   Queen
Tournament Forfeit
Checkmate   Score
King   Rank

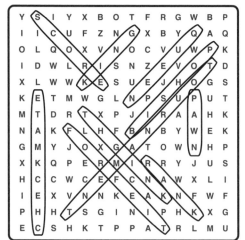

```
Y S I Y X B O T F R G W B P
I I C U F Z N G X B Y Q A Q
O L Q O X V N O C V U W P K
I D W L R I S N Z E V O T D
X L W W K E S U E J H O G S
K E T M W G L N P S U P U T
M T D R T X P J I R A A H K
N A K Y F L H F B N B Y W E K
G M Y J O X G A T O W N H P
X K Q P E R M I R R Y J U S
H C C W C E F C N A W X L I
I E X V N N K E A K N F W F
P H H T S G I N I P H K X G
E C S H K T P P A T R L M U
```

Page 223
State Birds

across		DOWN	
3	Michigan	1	Maryland
6	Iowa	2	Tennessee
8	California	4	Colorado
11	New Mexico	5	New York
12	Vermont	7	Indiana
		9	Georgia
		10	Arizona

Crossword solution:
- 1 down: ORIOLE
- 2 down: MOCKINGBIRD
- 3 across: ROBIN
- 4 down: BUNTING
- 5 down: BLUEBIRD
- 6 across: GOLDFINCH
- 7 down: CARDINAL
- 8 across: QUAIL
- 9 down: THRASHER
- 10 down: WREN
- 11 across: ROADRUNNER
- 12 across: THRUSH

Answers

Page 224
Dancing Diner

Page 225
Sudoku

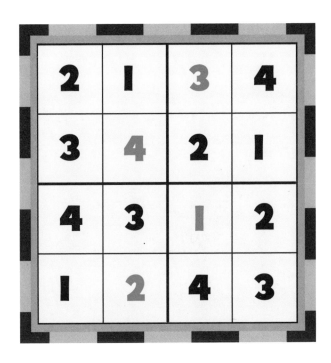

Page 226
Types of Cakes

Pound   Ice cream
Chocolate   Carrot
Shortcake   Red Velvet
Coffee   Birthday
Cheesecake   Wedding

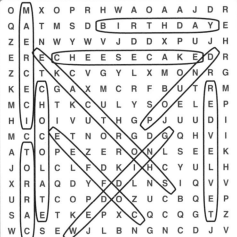

Page 227
USA Maze

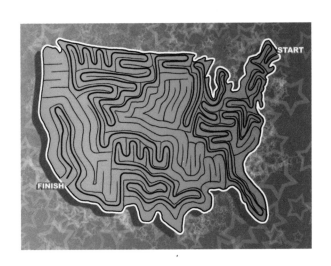

Answers

Page 228
Double Geese

Page 229
Decode-a-Riddle

A=!	E=%	I=(	M=:	Q=]	U='	Y=}
B=@	F=^	J=+	N=<	R="	V=?	Z={
C=#	G=&	K=)	O=>	S="	W=/	
D=$	H=*	L=;	P=[	T='	X=\	

W H E R E   D O E S
F R I D A Y   C O M E
B E F O R E   T H U R S D A Y ?

I N   T H E
D I C T I O N A R Y

Page 230
Technology

— NE + M +

— CK +   — WA

C O M P U T E R

Page 231
Out In Space

ACROSS
3 Our closest neighbor in space
4 The red planet
7 Chunk of a planet
8 The ringed planet

DOWN
1 Twinkling in the night sky
2 Source of light and heat
3 Our galaxy
4 The hottest planet
5 Streaks through space with a tail
6 The biggest planet